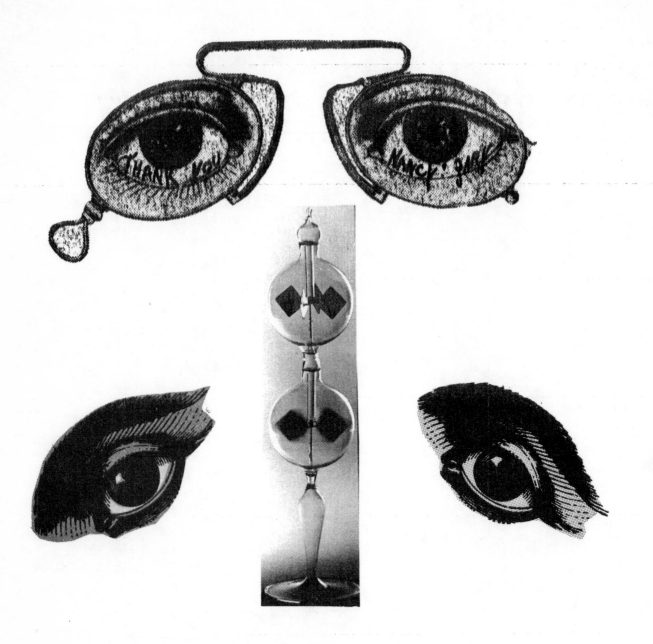

Photo of a sunvane* as was displayed in store windows by early optometrists, oculists and opticians (1890-1920), as an indication of their calling, profession, or vocation, including the decalcomania eye and the illuminated eyeglass sign hanging outside, not unlike the large gold tooth which once adorned the front of the dentist office or the barber pole for the surgeon-barber or the large flasks of colored fluid for the druggist.

EARLY AMERICAN *SPECS*

AN EXCITING COLLECTIBLE

Dr. L.D. Bronson

THE OCCIDENTAL PUBLISHING COMPANY

GLENDALE, CALIFORNIA 91204

TO B.B. and SHAUN

LIMITED EDITION
COPYRIGHT © 1974 by DR. L.D. BRONSON
PRINTED AND BOUND IN U.S.A.

LIBRARY of CONGRESS CATALOGUE CARD NO. 73-83399

ACKNOWLEDGEMENTS

I wish to express my appreciation to the following organizations and individuals, without whom the task of research, reviewing, editing and actual typing would have been unpredictable: Better Vision Institute, Bausch & Lomb Optical Co., William and Herbert Grossman, the late Dr. William Rohrer, Susan Sarof, John Campbell, Peter McNamara, American Optical Corporation, Mollie Sittner: Librarian, Visual Science Library, Los Angeles College of Optometry, L. DeGrave: Librarian, Bausch & Lomb Science Library, David Bresler (highly myopic) candidate, Ph. D., U.C.L.A., R.E. Powell, publisher of Optometric World, as well as Everett Jackson, medical specialist, Smithsonian Institution.

I wish to thank also my lovely wife, Beatrice, and my three wonderful daughters, Dana, Marci and Lori, for their help, encouragement and patience in suffering the numerous facets of my continuous involvements in divergent and extra-curricular activities.

"Right as a spectacle helpeth feeble sighte.

When a man on the book redith or writ."

Hoccleve 1415 A.D.

5

𝔠ONTENTS

INTRODUCTION

In Chinese symbolism, it was the Year of the Ox or the Boar or the Ram. Precisely, it was the year when our youth reacted to what they encountered all around them. . . . . . .and they rebelled.

It was an era of specialization in most endeavors. To wit: Eye specialists, Neurologists*, Cardiologists*, Proctologists** and the like, as well as collectors of antique barbed wire, bottle tops, old beer cans, glass insulators, match box covers, old PLAYBOY magazines, baby nursing bottles and other assorted memorabilia and/or trivia. . . . each possessed of its own lore.

This decade also witnessed a fragmentation of our society, a separation of social caste. The "establishment*" versus such groups as the "Hippies*", Black Panthers*, Weathermen*, Women's Lib*, Religious Rock* and an assortment of ethnic and political categories---a new society disjointment.

The so-called hippy groups embraced a movement of individualism which fostered, as part of its tenets, a complete rebellion against the accepted apparel of the day. The dress was either authentic colonial or a very excellent replica. The long flowing, high-necked gown embellished the female or else the close to the earth attire of shopworn and profusely patched blue jeans*, to the bare feet or heavy work-shoes, colonial hats, burlap handbags, tie-dyed undershirts ad infinitum. The apparel was in effect anything which could be termed rebellious or relating to what was considered a better era, a remnant of the good old times.

A similar attitude pervaded the field of eyewear. These new ethnic groups took to antique spectacles, the so-called ''Groovy Eyeglasses*'', or thin metal rims. If such spectacle frames were not to be obtained from their vision specialists, they turned to the local antique emporium or boutique shop, or else they scoured the flea markets* or swap meets*. If luck had it, grandma's attic spewed from its bossom another art treasure in the form of her old specs.

In his private optometric practice the author has encountered a flood of incidents where patients confronted him with their prized possession, an antique spectacle frame, a family heirloom, and with proud exuberance extolled its background evincing its lengthy and familial significance. Some of the spectacle frames were circa

**Engaged in rectal activities

*See the Glossary for definitions of unusual and technical terms and short dissertations on related subjects.

1865. The patients pleaded with the author to instruct his laboratory assistant to grind and insert their new prescription lenses into the antique frame. This kind of incident became a frequent occurrence after a short time.

These are the experiences which sparked the interest of the writer into compiling this guidebook. The author has been a practicing optometrist for over thirty years. His family history in optics dates back to the early 20th century. He has been an avid collector of Objets d'Art for many years; of course, antique eyeglasses have been at the top of his efforts. Many of the photos and illustrations are taken from his private collection. A number of newspaper and magazine articles have been written concerning his collection and how it relates to his private practice. Amongst his numerous transactions he has supplied eight pairs of authentic eyeglasses for the Hall of Presidents*, an attraction at the new Disneyworld situated in Orlando Beach, Florida; a 400 million dollar complex. He has also fitted and advised the correct eyewear or reproductions for character actors who use them in theatrical productions. With this group the author has used a Polaroid type camera, and within five minutes the actor can appraise the effect with the addition of the spectacles.

A situation occurred, most recently, which further provoked the author's interest to a more immediate response. He decided to pay a visit to the Visual Science Library of the Southern California College of Optometry to research the dates of some of his newer specimens. He requested a book on Early American Eyeglasses and was told that the only formal writing on the subject was dated 1915. He found this to be included in the American Encyclopedia of Ophthalmology. In addition, he was handed a few sundry pamphlets which alluded to the origin of spectacles in general--one in Japanese, one in French and one in German. The librarian, obviously curious about his present project, remarked that she had wished someone would write a book on antique eyeglasses as she and her staff receive requests for the classification of both American and foreign "specs." "The library urgently needs such a reference book."

The librarian was familiar with some of the author's past scientifically oriented literary contributions. Her apparent appeal precipitated an end to his indecisiveness. His activities were immediately directed toward this new goal.

One of the obvious good things resulting from the transformation experienced by our new society relates to a reversal of the classic cliche, "Men don't make passes at girls who wear glasses." The female, at present, prefers to wear glasses. Wearing glasses has become the *in thing* and they are worn probably as much for the *cause* as for the therapy; as an ecological intonation directed to the preservation of the good things of the earth.

The motif of the spectacle could be considered a gauge to indicate the feelings of the era. It may be serving a dual capacity: its primary function in vision, and a secondary function as a chronical of the emotional stature of the times--sort of a *visual yardstick*.

This offering in book form will endeavor to make a sincere effort to set forth the essential factors concerning both the recent interest and its accompanying demand, to arrange systematically all pertinent factors into an easy and ready reference, all concerning early American spectacles, eyeglasses, oxfords, lorgnettes and quizzers*. Reference to a few foreign specimens will be for reasons historical and prototypical.

The inhabitants of Early America were far too engrossed in simple survival to indulge greatly in hobbies. True, some gathered Indian arrowheads and similar relics with their hunting trophies. This condition did not change until the end of the 17th century. The New World sprouted only a few collectors of books, since all these were imported, hence, expensive and rare.

The need for maximum visual efficiency was not as demanding in colonial days. Sculptors, painters, artisans and the like produced only what their visual skills permitted. Obviously, it sufficed. They interpolated what they saw to their creative performance. Example: El Greco, who was said to have suffered with high a stigmatism, painted the elongated figures so evident in his technique and styling.

The author was of speaking acquaintance with Atillio Piccarilli, an eminent sculptor who, at the time, was past seventy years of age. The author was intrigued by the masterful quality of his work despite his lack of any visual assistance. This is a rarity with individuals who do close work and are aged. Mr. Piccarilli replied, when questioned about this, "I am afraid if I see better I will find too many faults, and my work might suffer."

Genuine antique original spectacles which are considered rare and unique are still in existence. However, most of these can be found only in national museums or are owned by outstanding collectors who have passed them on from generation to generation as the prize family possession, mainly in families associated with optics or the ophthalmic* professions. Suffice to say that these are rarely found in circulation. This book will delve into their specifications and characteristics and present an historical generalization of such known unique specimens. It would appear unrealistic to attempt to collect spectacles so rare and is tantamount to offering to purchase a prized Rembrandt from a museum or collection where it is housed.

A discussion of the origin of all spectacles in general will precede the actual investigation of those where a possibility of collecting still exists and where authentic originals are still available. In particular, reference will be made to the era dating around the period of Ben Franklin*, who gave so much, including the invention of the bifocal spectacle: to wit, a representation of collectibles from the 18th century to the present.

The availability of antique eyeglasses may appear to have reached a saturation point when the usual sources report that they are now "hard to come by." However, fine specimens still can be found if the collector is diligent in his efforts.

The greater majority of antique spectacles which are retrieved for the purpose of being made functional have long been in disuse. Many are in dire need of restoration by competent craftsmen or optical laboratory technicians who are familiar with all ophthalmic appliances. Those which are to be restored and reused often require refurb-

ishing with new screws, temples* or nose pads. There are only a limited number of craftsmen who can replace broken or missing parts from old stocks. Otherwise, replicas of such parts must be forged from the raw material.

A great percentage of precious metal frames has been put out of circulation because of their gold and silver content. These were melted down as "scrap." This practice was accelerated by the continued increase in their metal value as a result of the recall of all gold coins in 1934 and the rising gold prices of 1973. Many used spectacles are sent to depressed areas, both at home and in foreign countries, where the frames are repaired and newly-reworked lenses, sorted from a stock of used lenses, are fitted to the frames and re-employed to improve the vision of the indigent. The foregoing factors have served only to moderate the availability of antique "specs".

Following the year 1880 many spectacles were of saddle bridge* construction. The hall-mark was usually stamped on the inner face of the bridge, obviously receiving the greatest amount of wear since it comes in continuous contact with the bridge of the nose, thus obliterating the markings which include the percentage of gold or silver content, the hallmark and the name of the manufacturer. Many frames cannot now be identified or classified accurately because of that practice. Many of the antique spectacles, especially those of even older vintage, are entirely unmarked. Some bear the focus mark only. Wherever possible in this book, all relevant researched information is given. The author has spent considerable effort to effect some semblance of order and classification.

America, in total, is some four centuries old, the United States only two centuries. It is the newest of great nations. It is consistent in its ideals with respect to social, economic and political institutions. It is the oldest republic, the oldest democracy and follows the oldest written constitution in the world. Hence, how old can an American antique be?

Theoretically, an antique is any item made prior to 1830. American industry at the time was of small consequence. When a piece of houseware was worn or broken it was usually relegated to what was considered a useful purpose, the fire heap. There was no attic or garage available, nor was there any desire or inclination to store *worthless trivia*, such as threadbare utensils or worn-out *curios*, like spectacles. Whatever was unknowingly salvaged can be found now mainly in museums. Whoever possesses even an inconsequential item treasures his heirloom and would part with it only under duress of inheritance perplexities or personal pecuniary embarrassment.

Collectibles, on the other hand, may be anything old or funky* and even dated as late a vintage as before 1930. Many antique shops and their recent extension, the *head shops* and boutiques, carry a vast array of such oddities including spectacles of the same circa. These are presently in greatest demand. Many of these were produced after 1930. Among such assortments of collectibles are often found authentic specimens at a ridiculously low price.

Most foreign antiques are identified and classified by reigning monarchs: Early Victorian, Mid-Victorian, Georgian, late Edwardian, Louis Bonaparte, etc. Since our very beginnings we have never experienced the might of the sceptor, or life under an autocratic government. The author has been provoked to separate periods of identification of antique "specs" by employing American wars as the line of demarcation rather than our heads of state, our presidents, who usually serve four to eight years. It has been known that wars accompany restrictions and the need for changes resulting from the substitutions imposed. Wars have a great influence on creativity and production; consequently periods of "specs" are listed

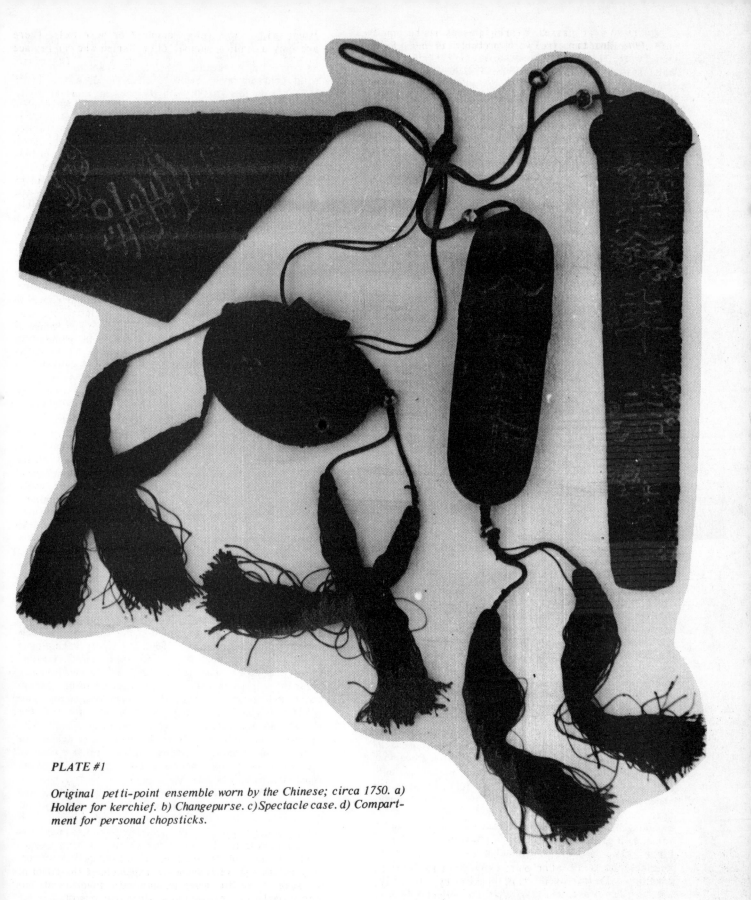

PLATE #1

Original petti-point ensemble worn by the Chinese; circa 1750. a) Holder for kerchief. b) Changepurse. c) Spectacle case. d) Compartment for personal chopsticks.

under The Revolutionary War (1775-1783), War of Eighteen Twelve (1812-1814), Mexican War (1846-1848), Civil War (1861-1865), Indian Wars (1869-1892), Spanish-American War (1898), World War I (1914-1918), World War II (1939-1945), Korean War (1950-1953) and the Vietnamese Conflict (circa 1962-1973).

Historians have observed repeatedly that there appears to be some semblance of symmetry or "M.O.*" with respect to the occurrence of wars in the United States and that wars bring about significant changes which some may call progress and others retrogression. Wars assuredly have had a tremendous impact on spectacle production. To wit: air corps goggles, gas mask eyeglasses and G.I.'s ("these G.I. glasses just don't cut it") circa Vietnamese War, see chapter, "Era of Groovy Eyeglasses." Glasses worn by our troops during the Indian Wars had a governmental U.S. Army imprint stamped on the front of the saddle bridge.

An antique spectacle or eyeglass must be in good condition to command top price. This policy stems from its present functional value and the usual practical approach of collectors in general. A rare or unique antique generally looses a considerable amount of its intrinsic and esthetic value if it is unrepairable. The lenses in the more recent specimens may be broken since these can easily be replaced. Lenses of an older vintage are of antique value themselves and should be intact. The repairability factor is one of the reasons for the scarcity of older plastic frames. Plastic eyerims cannot be cemented if broken, even with modern epoxy cements. The pressure needed to hold a lense in place makes cementing eyerims futile. Metal frames can be brazed or even soldered. Such parts as temples, hinges, pads and screws present only slight problems in replacement.

It is true that there are those select scions of *bakery* families with plenty of "bread"*, who wish to become ardent collectors of antiques of a level where purchases can be made of a silver soup tureen on stand, George III by Paul Storr*, London circa 1812, priced at $20,000.00 or a silver teapot by the same silversmith, circa 1821, for $35,000.00 or Sheffield inkstands, circa 1810, for $500.00. The collection of antique "specs", however, is still "wide open" and low priced. Those who grasp at the opportunity will glean many hours of pleasurable appreciation.

The frequency and vastness of the institution of the antique show in our present society is overshadowed only by the author's feeling of remorse and emptiness when contemplating the scarcity of the showing of antique spectacles as a collectible. A visit to any of the larger antique shows will substantiate this definitve statement of fact. A participant will find only a few specimens on exhibit or for sale. The prices will be found to be twofold in nature; some extremely low and others unreasonably high. At the Devonshire Downs show on December 2nd, 3rd, 4th and 5th of 1971, a scout was fortunate to find seven pairs of spectacles on display in the entire show. One was offered at $15.00 in a sterling silver spectacles case holding an A.O. "Fits-U* finger piece mounting". It was the spectacle case which really had the value. Two pair were bought for $7.35, one an "innerim"* circa 1925 and one a thin metal oval yellow gold-filled spectacle circa 1912, both of which were in excellent condition and a terrific buy. The third purchase was really *one for the books*, a solid gold 10kt A.O. "varsity*" beautifully engraved oxford and chain. The asking price was $25.00, but it was bought for $20.00. The period represented by this piece was circa 1905. Its present estimated value is $150.00.

An unbelievable price disparity was evident. This is a realistic and concrete example of the existing ignorance regarding a correct price structure. A further amplifi-

cation of the last paragraph; at one booth the scout was offered a gold-filled Fits-U eyeglass circa 1915 for $15.00; its correct present value is about $5.00 At another booth the solid gold engraved oxford*, circa 1905, asking price $25.00, sold for $20.00; with its present value at easily $150.00. The author is confident this book will offer some solution to a correct evaluation of a collectible "spec."

In the well attended antique show of June 13-17, 1973, held at the Santa Monica Civic Auditorium, the writer found only one pair of spectacles and case C. 1850; material of construction nickle-silver. The price asked was $29.50. Lorgnettes were more abundant since they are still functional and appeal to female liberationists, possibly to be used as a baton when needed or else as an expression of their chauvinism.

The writer was able to pick up a 14Kt solid gold lorgnette for $55.00. The identical lorgnette displayed at another booth commanded an asking price of $125.00. An aggregate count of seven other lorgnettes were shown. Obviously this is no show of a representative abundance or a concerted interest.

But wait! A serious conversation with one of the more prominent dealers disclosed the scarcity of such specimens. They simply have vanished from the market like the gold coin. People are hedging with valuable collectibles especially those smaller of size. This financial situation has been brought about because of our unstable currency. A great percentage of lorgnettes were fabricated in precious metals, many studded with high quality gem stones including diamonds.

The antique spectacle case is a specialized item which can consume the full interest of an individual, as a separate collectible. Those of older vintage are of excellent handicraft; they are all handmade, of course. Leather, wood, cloth, metal, tortoise shell set with pearls, gold and silver, set with gem stones. Pearl inlaids were sometimes set with diamonds or other precious gems. Considerable effort went into the design and production. Some cases were designed to hang from a chatelaine in an arrangement in which an ornamental clasp was worn by a lady at the waist. The eyeglass case was fastened to the chatelaine by two lengths of chain from which it was suspended. Both the clasp and the case were often highly decorated. Some forged from precious metals like silver and gold. The less ornate consisted of a metal clasp and a finely tooled leather case, circa 1880. The Spencer catalogue dated 1880 illustrated item #282 page 70, "Silk Plush Chatelaine cases, assorted colors" priced at $7.50 per dozen. The present asking price ranges between $15.00 and $50.00 for the leather. The silver could easily bring $75.00; the gold $200.00 or more. This type of case is the rarest and because of its great esthetic appeal could command any inflated price. In our present scheme of things, some of the finest shops display expensive boudoir sets which invariably contain a spectacle case. These cases alone often retail for $25.00.

In an effort to avert being repetitious, some plates contain groupings of similar models. The author would like nothing better than to describe and portray each specimen separately; demon monotony, however, may show its ugly head and dull reading might ensue.

The usual book on antiques is both proper and prim. In this offering the author has attempted to interest all readers. He has tried to present the subject matter in a simple, up-to-date vein, directed to appeal to all areas of the population although with particular attention to collectors and potential collectors.

All photographs used in this book are from the original optical appliances "in situ." They are not reprints, except for several obvious reprints so noted and including one painted by H. Sonderman (1864).

The author at this time wishes to direct the attention

of the reader to the glossary. This contains thumb-nail sketches of much pertinent information and should make interesting reading.

The two chapters which follow are mainly historical. An attempt has been made to intersperse this usual duller reading with lively vignettes in an effort to foster greater reader's interest. The impatient folk or those who do not "dig" history can readily skip over this portion and onto the meatier subject matter.

The philosophical remarks punctuating the subject matter should be considered in the light of prosaic license.

Advertisement of equipment as appeared in catalogue # 9, Spencer Optical Manufacturing Company, 15 Maiden Lane, New York City, New York — Circa 1890.

Present updated Automated Refractor costs $16,000.00.

Reproduction of address on package mailed to the author.

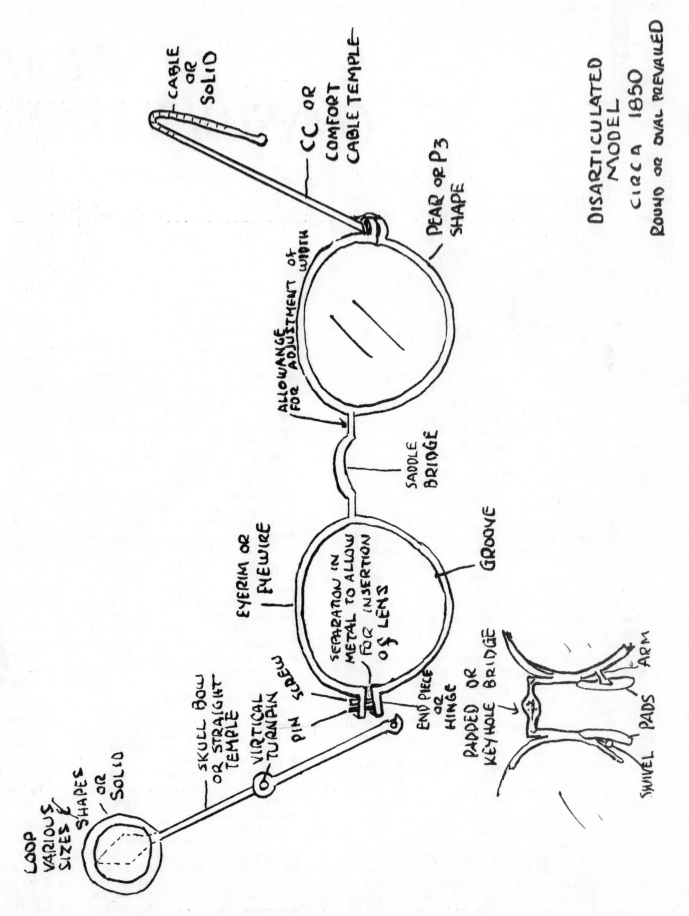

CABLE OR SOLID

CC OR COMFORT CABLE TEMPLE

PEAR OR P3 SHAPE

ALLOWANCE FOR ADJUSTMENT OF WIDTH

SADDLE BRIDGE

EYERIM OR EYEWIRE

SEPARATION IN METAL TO ALLOW FOR INSERTION OF LENS

GROOVE

SKULL BOW OR STRAIGHT TEMPLE

VIRTICAL TURNPIN PIN SCREW

END PIECE OR HINGE

PADDED OR KEYHOLE BRIDGE

SWIVEL PADS ARM

LOOP VARIOUS SIZES & SHAPES OR SOLID

DISARTICULATED MODEL
CIRCA 1850
ROUND OR OVAL PREVAILED

1

GENERAL CONSIDERATION

In the language of the vision specialist the word spectacles refers to a division of eyeglasses where the front section is held in place on the nose by two temples* or arms, one on each side of the head encircling the ears or hugging the skull. This is opposed to an eyeglass, which is held in place by a spring device called either a finger-piece mounting* or a one-piece mounting*. The latter is sometimes known as a hoop-spring mounting. The two terms spectacle and eyeglasses are commonly confused and used interchangeably. A further distinction can be made in the construction and material of the spectacle. It can be fabricated in plastic (tortoise-shell appearing, but synthetic) and offered in a great variety of colors and decor, also in all-metal frames and metal-plastic combination* or rimless, and rimless with a protective bar across the top (Numont* or Rimway*).

A third classification could be considered decorative rather than functional. This category numbers within its milieu the oxford*, either folding or non-folding, and the lorgnette*. The material of fabrication of this third group may be of the most precious metal, such as platinum, highly ornamented, set with expensive gems and embellished with fine engraving, enamelling and filigree work. Many of the first forms of eyewear were related to this category and were made of material available at the time, such as tortoise shell, leather, wood, bone, horn, rubber, paper mache, amber*, gutta percha* and other basic materials.

A fourth category could be the quizzer*, magnifier, monocle or single lens device. The quizzer antedated all eyewear. The first form of visual aid was of monolenticular construction, a religiously oriented burning glass filled with water which could easily have served an additional purpose as a magnifying or reading glass. This is known to have been used in the late 13th century. An explanation of this will follow later in this chapter.

An appliance for the correction of refractive errors* (errors of vision) or eye-muscle imbalance* contains two main components. First, the ophthalmic lenses and, secondly, a device to support the lenses in a fashion conducive to vision in comfort. A latter day third complex is the contact lens. The conventional hard type, and the soft type of more recent vintage, will be touched on lightly since its own history is voluminous. See the chapter entitled RING ON THE FINGER.

It can be said that this is an entirely new area of operation for collectors. As a field it is, by and large, esthetic and functional as well as therapeutic. Interest in this new area has "snowballed." If the esthetic value of a collectible can be evaluated by its demand and the collector's relative increase in a feeling of euphoria, then this field of interest must head the list for its continued appreciation. For those who seek monetary aggrandizement as their primary objective, quoting the rise in bidding price for a sought-after item would be sufficient. Let us say, for example, a 10 kt or a 14 kt yellow solid gold oval thin rim metal spectacle, circa 1912, is priced in the Sears-Roebuck catalogue at $2.60 and $3.50 respectively. In 1966, the going price was $5.50 and $6.50. Recent offered prices in antique shops were between $50.00 and $75.00 and were rising rapidly. A solid gold 14kt lorgnette circa 1920 sold to the vendor for $25.00. In 1960 the author paid between $15.00 and $20.00; the most recent asking price is from $150.00 to $400.00. The service of a computer would be required to estimate the relative per centum of continuous increase.

In an effort to accentuate the high cost of spectacle frames of this present era Plate #1 shows reproductions of frames expressly created for the quality and style-conscious public. The cost of these may appear exorbitant. However, there are those who have the "bread" and the price is no object.

	Present Wholesale Cost	Approximate Retail Price
Fantasia	10kt solid gold - $295.00	$425.00
	14kt solid gold - $325.00	$500.00
Edinburgh	10kt solid gold - $130.00	$230.00
	14kt solid gold - $255.00	$325.00

These prices were quoted prior to the rising price of gold during 1973.

Other imported frames constructed from precious metals and ornamented with diamonds and secondary stones of gem quality can be found to cost from $550.00 to 12,000.00 for each frame. Assuredly we cannot allay this dramatic rise in cost to the dollar devaluation of 1972 and 1973.

It is still possible today to find antique frames of like metallic weight and quality but lower in price and of finer craftsmanship than the Fantasia and Edinburgh.

Elegance in Gold By BOIC

Model FANTASIA

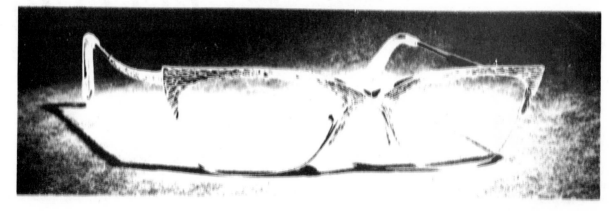

Here is supreme harmony of inspired design and mature optical craftsmanship. The crisp browline is flattering to most facial types, and the beautifully engraved front is enhanced by two burnished flashes above the bridge.

Model EDINBURGH

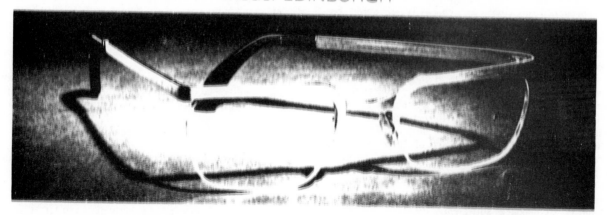

A frame for the man demanding opulence with dignity. Strongly constructed and neat in appearance, EDINBURGH is a must for modern top men.

Authentic artists rendering (1920) of spectacles worn by George Washington. Note high decor.

HISTORICAL EFFLUVIA

It has been pointed out previously that eyewear in general is composed of the sum total of two main components. It would not be remiss here to present a short historical discussion of the therapeutic portion: the lens made of glass, and followed by the supporting fixture-the frame.

Glass was not used for the purpose of making lenses until comparatively recent years. The only suitable substances which could be found were rock crystal, quartz, topaz, emerald, beryl or any naturally transparent homogeneous stone which could be mined and whose basic form approached convexity or concavity or could be altered easily to these forms. Sections of quartz used as lenses were called *pebbles*. The German word "brille" (spectacle) is derived from the word "beryl", a clear rock formation.

The true origin of what we know of glass has been lost to antiquity. One of the earliest chemical products made by man was glass. Pliny (A.D. 23-79), an ancient scientific writer, ascribed its discovery to a group of Phoenician sailors who were shipwrecked on a sandy shore. They used a block of natron*, part of their cargo, to support a kettle hung over an improvised fire. The heat fused the sand with the natron and "voila!" glass was discovered. The authenticity of this occurrence is truly questionable since we are aware that it is a physical impossibility to produce sufficiently elevated temperatures for sand to fuse. To perform this feat requires a minimum temperature of 3,000° F., more than can be effected by a bonfire. Even though this tale is obviously fictional, at least it demonstrates how early in history glass was known and discussed in literature.

It is most probable that the place of origin of glass was Ancient Egypt and the Phoenecians obtained their knowledge of glass from the workers on the banks of the Old Nile. Modern archeologists, however, have unearthed, in tombs, evidence of the existence of articles made of glass as far back as the fifth and sixth dynasties some 3300 years before Christ.

Glass was used for optical purposes in the form of a burning glass during the Neolithic and Mesopotamian Civilizations and employed for religious purposes "to bring down fire from heaven." The word *focus* (Latin) meant originally a hearth or burning place. One may note that the modern French word "foyer" is used for both "hearth" and "focus." An entry in the *Inventory of the Vestry,* Westminster Abbey, in 1388, makes mention of the practice of kindling the new fire on Easter Eve by the use of a burning glass. A device sufficiently effective to concentrate incident light, as used in a burning glass, could readily be used as a magnifying or reading glass.

At the time the belief was that the water and not the glass was possessed of divine powers. Knowledge now exists that refraction is determined by the passage of light from a media of one index to another. In this instance the passage was from air to glass. The water served to bend the light only slightly.

Neither glass nor glassmaking assumed much importance until the invention of the blowpipe by some forgotten benefactor of mankind during the second or third century B.C. During the latter part of the 18th century, until about 1940 when restrictions were imposed, many sunglass lenses were made by blowing a large colored bubble of glass and then dividing this into segments sufficiently large to serve as what we called coquille lenses. The lens so produced was quite aberrated, affording only harmfully distorted vision. Most governments have banned the use of coquille lenses.

There are two principle kinds of glass: lime is used in one together with other ingredients. This combination is called "crown glass." The other is produced with an oxide of lead as one of the ingredients and is known as "flint glass." Most lenses are now ground from crown glass blanks.

In the Egyptian section of the British Museum a principal exhibit displays two magnifying glasses which would have made excellent burning glasses except for their aging and resultant tarnish. These were ground and polished. One was found in Tanis and correctly date 150 A.D. Conclusive proof was established in 1927 by E.J. Forsdyke concerning two crystal magnifying lenses that dated back at least as early as 1200 B.C. and probably 1600 B.C.

In 1038 Alhazen supposedly ground a magnifying lens* using sand as the abrasive and a piece of thick glass pane as the metal. The finished lens was held in such a manner as to enable him to bring the fine lines of his scroll larger in order to accommodate for the degradation of his age-dimmed eyes. Alhazen, probably the greatest scientist of his day, an Egyptian born in 965 A.D., wrote, "If an object is placed at the base of the larger segment of a glass it will appear magnified."

Ophthalmic lenses today are ground and polished by a method not too far removed from the time of Alhazen. The molten glass is poured into metal moulds which are approximately the diameter and curvature of the finished product. Afterward follows a timed cooling process which anneals the glass. These blanks are ground with assorted fine abrasives and polished to transparency with a heat producing compound, usually a metal oxide, cerium.

The first corroborated mention of the use of spectacles appeared near the end of the 13th century in the works of Meissner (1260-1280), who expressly stated that old people derive an advantage from spectacles. Nicolas Bullet,

Plate 2

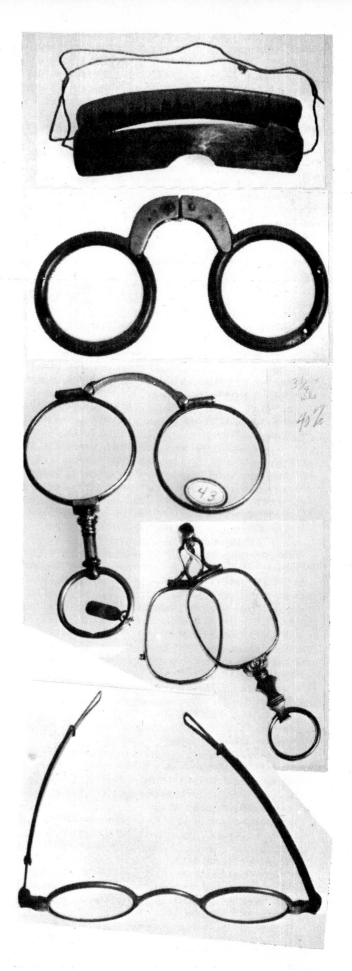

1. *Spectacles: Sunvisor; Eskimo; handmade carved form wood; dated 19th century.*

2. *Spectacles: Chinese wood rims (folding); held in place by silk cords; dated 600 A.C. Author's note: (Smithsonian dating questionable; invention of spectacles, outside China walls, thought to be late 13th century). . .see text. . .Author estimated date more like 1600 A.D. Spectacles worn for other than visual purposes in China.*

3. *Lorgnettes: Folding gold plated; bridge hinged for folding. Author's estimate-- circa 1825.*

4. *Lorgnette: Folding gold plated; circa 1840. Author believes this to be solid gold because of hand engraving or at least silver, gold plated.*

5. *Spectacles: Heavy silver frames; sliding extension temples with open tips; elliptical lenses; marked--McAllister, Philad. Dated CA. 1780.*

a priest, used spectacles in 1282 when signing an agreement. The invention of spectacles for the short and long sighted is mentioned as a discovery in a manuscript, dated 1299, in Florence. Nevertheless, the circumstances surrounding the incident of the invention or development of spectacles is shrouded in mystery and probably lost forever.

Numerous historical reports have been explored, some obvious fantasies, some approaching a reality. A statement of many of these will follow. The reader will most certainly concede to an existing disparity.

Nero is the most prominent of the names in earliest history connected with these incredible debacles. The *fiddler* supposedly employed a large emerald in the form of a "quizzer*" as a visual aid. Other tales are indicative of his morbid fear of bright lights and blood. Nero apparently used the emerald to mitigate his psychosis rather than improve his sight. Looking through the emerald his eye perceived an image which served to lessen the tumultuous display in the arena before him and transformed the gaping wounds and the flowing blood of the combatants to the less revolting black imagery.

Until recently Salvino d'Armato of Florence, who died in 1317, was presumed to be the inventor of spectacles. A marble bust erected in a churchyard in Florence carries his epitaph which reads, "Inventor of spectacles-God pardon him his sins." It has been disclosed that such a person never existed. The Armato family had put claim to the invention and erected the monument to a fictitious relative in an effort to secure glory for the family and Florence.

At about the same time, the Friar Alessandro Spina of Pisa, who died in 1313 and who had the reputation of being an expert craftsman and possessing an extraordinary acumen for reproducing mechanical devices, had seen some early eyeglasses, duplicated them and shared his knowledge with a willing heart -- in contrast to di-Armato who supposedly refused to disclose the particulars of his invention.

Research has shown similar claims for the Chinese, Marco Polo*, the Greeks, Egyptians, French, Germans, and the Spanish. The Israelites of biblical times had little use for any visual aid. They are reputed to have committed their teachings to memory and passed them on from mouth to mouth.

Spectacle frames, even without lenses, were considered a badge of superior social status and learning among the Chinese. An interesting etiquette has grown out of this symbolism; an inferior had to remove his glasses in the presence of his superior, especially if they were oversized. This custom survived in Germany as late as the year 1915. The wearing of frames glazed with even afocal (non-prescription) lenses is still regarded as a sign of higher intelligence in many sections of the world. In China the size of the frames was meant to be an indication of the academic status of the wearer. This was a stimulus to the Orientals to *out-size* the Europeans in their eyewear, hence establishing a relative evaluation of their superior mental ability.

A Chinese emperor is said to have used tortoise shell glasses in 2283 B.C. The tortoise was glorified as a sacred animal by the Chinese; hence, their interpretation that the wearing of tortoise shell rimmed glasses would convey good fortune and long life. At one point of Chinese history the emperor could distinguish his subject's station in society only by the size of the spectacles worn -- the larger the lens size, the higher the rank.

Throughout the centuries spectacles were used as a status symbol. Their worth was considered of such great importance that they were passed on by royalty to the next of kin in their last testaments. As early as 1379 the will of Charles V of France bequeathed, "two pair of glasses of black horn rims and a wooden handle, one

of gold with a large silver carrying case weighing 10 pounds."

It is not too remote a thought to consider that during the thirteenth and fourteenth centuries the belief that using spectacles to aid in reading was considered work of the devil. In fact, the printing of books was looked at with great trepidity by Lorenzo de' Medici, scion of a most influential family in Italy. Hand-lettered manuscripts were thought to be of superior workmanship and were prized for their beauty of script and their rarity of composition.

As recently as 1971, in an article published in the British Journal of Ophthalmology and written by Rishi Kumar Agarwal -- obviously of Hindu extraction, attests to the invention of spectacles as being in India between 1344 and 1353, probably by the Kannorda - speaking Hindu, and that the use of lenses reached Europe via the Arabs. His claim expounds the theory that the European records of the origin of spectacles are mostly controversial, hence substantiating his claim.

As for the making of lenses, Roger Bacon, the unconventional English father of science, indicated in "Opus Majus" which was completed in 1268 A.D. that, "by placing a segment of a transparent body on a book with the plain side down, small letters will appear larger. This application can be useful to the aged and those with weakened eyes." He described convex reading lenses accompanied by drawings. He also made reference to concave lenses. The latter were apparently left in abeyance or relegated to the work of later scientists.

Portraits of men of reknown *(never of women)* often showed the subject wearing glasses. The artist ignored the calendar and frequently portrayed a subject wearing glasses in biblical times, when they were non-existent, as a symbol of intellect. A miniature of Moses wearing spectacles was painted in Germany in 1452; this is obviously an anachronism. The earliest painting to show eyeglasses is that of Hugh of Providence done by Tommoso de Modiana in 1352.

Artists depicted glasses to have existed as far back as the Garden of Eden without thought of their authenticity. On a Spanish tapestry called "Creation of Eve", an aged priest is portrayed with glasses perched on his nose. The "Death of the Virgin" shows an apostle wearing pince-nez. A painting of the infant Jesus in his mother's arms has the baby holding a pair of glasses, which apparently belong to his father, Joseph, who is pictured in the background.

In 1480 Domenico Gherlandaio painted St. Jerome with a pair of glasses dangling on a string from around his neck. This painting started a rumor that the saint had invented eyeglasses. The belief in the saint's inventive ability persisted and St. Jerome emerged as the patron saint of spectacle makers. This guild of spectacle makers received its first charter in 1563 in England. The Worshipful Company of Spectacle Makers was the royal nomenclature granted later in a charter to artisans in England who were engaged in the production of all types of visual aids. King Charles I was the reigning monarch in the year 1629. This charter gave the group great power to control the opticians of that time, and is still in effect. It is considered the oldest and most widely known of its kind in the world.

In the 15th century, following Gutenberg's development* of moveable type and the inception of the manufacture of inexpensive newsprint, a social revolution occurred with people noticing the printed word. Those with defective near vision realized the dire need for some form of visual aid.

In 1550 Leonardo da Vinci* was engaged in gathering a considerable amount of information regarding the principles of optics. A description of a prototype contact lens was part of this study. In 1575 Maurolycus published

NEW STYLE SPECTACLE SIGNS

These signs are absolutely waterproof, being made from metal, heavily painted and gilded. The panels are metal with a handsome eye painted on each.

The outside lines represent space for name.

18 inch, as represented in cut $3.00
24 "   "   " 4.50
30 "   "   " 6.00
36 "   "   " 7.25

Name and business neatly lettered in red on outside space, $1.00 extra.

a book on optics which contained a discussion of near-sightedness and farsightedness.

The earliest illustrated scientific work on the use of spectacles was furnished in 1623 by Daza de Valdes of Seville, a clergyman. The first formal tables for sight testing were part of the 100 printed pages of the manuscript. It was the first clinical approach to our present procedure for eye testing.

The oldest pair of spectacles in excellent preservation is housed in the Nuremberg Museum. The spectacle is dated about the time Christopher Columbus is said to have invaded America.

The original spectacles worn by both Benjamin Franklin and George Washington are in perfect preservation and on display at The Franklin Institution, Philadelphia, and at Mount Vernon, New York respectively. This fact alone is evidence of the tremendous impact on our history made by spectacles. During the era of Benjamin Franklin some iron-rimmed spectacles were constructed with a protective rim of horn between the metal and the lens. Its function was to cushion the glass and thereby minimize breakage of the lens. This attempt at producing a safety or impact resistant mechanism has been repeated during a number of different periods in the history of specs. However, the author's contribution to the development and perfection of a plastic spectacle lens around 1954, has been of obvious momentous impact. In January of 1972 the Food and Drug Administration made impact resistant lenses mandatory. (See chapter on safety lenses.)

In 1838 a book was published by Haswell, Barrington and Haswell of Philadelphia, written by J.G. Millingen, M.D., entitled Curiosities of Medical Experiences. The table of contents contains dissertations on such incredible oddities as Somnambulism, Phrenology, Demonomania, leeches, spectacles, animal magnetism, on flagellation, affections of the sight and on dreams. In total the book contains some 75 chapters on what appears to be an inordinate accumulation of what our present academicians would term phantasmagorial.

The chapter on ''Spectacles'' is only a half-page in text and follows:

The origin of these valuable instruments is uncertain: that the ancients were acquainted with the laws of refraction is beyond all doubt, since they made use of glass globes filled with water to produce combustion; and in Seneca we find the following very curious passage ''Litterae, quamvis minutae et obscurae, per vitream pilam aqua plenam majores clarioresque cernuntur.'' Yet thirteen centuries elapsed ere spectacles were known. It is supposed that they were first invented by Salvino or Salvino Armati; but he kept his discovery secret until Alessandro de Spina, a monk in Pisa, brought them into use in 1313. Salvino was considered their inventor, from the epitaph on his tomb in the cathedral church in Florence: ''Qui giace Salvino D'Armato, degl'Armati de Firenze, inventor delli occhiali, ec. 1317.'' Another cirumstance seems to add weight to this presumption: Luigi Sigoli, a contemporary artist, in a painting of the Circumcision, represents the high-priest Simeon with a pair of spectacles, which, from his advanced age, it was supposed he might have needed on the occasion.

The chapter ''Affections of the Sight'' refers to difficulties in vision as a ''Vitiated condition'' and divides such into six categories: night sight, day sight, long sight, short sight, skew sight, and false sight. The most interesting connotation describes ''long sight'' as being indicative of enlarged pupils and remedied by ''convex glasses'' and ''short sight'' where the iris is contracted and, therefore, spectacles of an opposite character, with concave lenses, are necessary. The fact that reference to the pupillary size is incorrectly stated is not as significant as the early representation of the correct lens requirement for Hyperopia* and Myopia* (long and short sight).

Primitive spectacles were crudely made. Refinement of construction appeared only when technology improved and not until the beginning of the 20th century. Spectacles were, at first, very expensive, costing from $100.00 to $200.00. From an economic standpoint only the rich were able to afford them. This added considerably to the prestige of the spectacle and they were valued highly because of this factor.

Throughout history repetition will be noted of the distinct relationship existing between the wearing of spectacles and the wearer who is invariably indentified with the literate class or as a member of the higher echelons of society -- as a status symbol -- or one seeking to be elevated to a class of significant prestige -- to a level of culture.

It has been brought to light recently that Vincent Van Gogh, the famous modern artist (1905), must have suffered an eye condition technically called Glaucoma, which is quite painful. History has indicated that Van Gogh suffered from a great deal of pain in the eyes. This statement is substantiated as evidenced by his paintings where lights and the sun are pictured, in that all these portray halos around the lights. One of the principle symptoms of Glaucoma is the halo seen around lights by those so afflicted. Very little was known about Glaucoma in 1905. How much more fruitful would his work have been if Glaucoma had been understood more fully at that time? His apparent suicide might also have been averted.

In 1903 the OPTICAL JOURNAL contained a drawing of a chicken wearing a pair of spectacles. These serve a definite and useful purpose. It appears that a chicken has some fixation about another chicken who may be oozing blood from some part of its anatomy. Chickens are known to peck at the sight of such blood letting until they completely destroy the afflicted bird. It has been found that by fitting all chickens with spectacles not unlike blinders and glazed with red lenses of thin plastic, these attacks on their ill-fated brethren are decimated.

In the classics of literature there will be frequently found some degree of importance attached to the advantage of spectacles in a particular situation. In Jonathan Swift's Gulliver's Travels published anonymously in 1727, when Swift was 60 years of age (age of presbyopia) he wrote, ''The Emperor of the Lilliputians'' ordered an inventory of his pockets which contained pistols etc. and, ''I had as I before observed, one private pocket which escaped their search; where there was a pair of spectacles (which I sometimes use for the weakness of mine eyes).''

Rudyard Kipling, in his famous Kim (copyrighted in 1900), wrote, ''Ay, ay! The lama mounted a pair of horn-rimmed spectacles of Chinese work. Here is the little door through which we bring wood before winter.'' In the book the lama continued to express his reactions to what he sees through the spectacles. The curator realized that the lama was no mendicant, but a scholar of parts. ''Later. . . .The lama taking snuff, wiping his spectacles and talking at railway speed.''

William Shakespeare, the bard of Stradford, invariably referred to spectacles in many of his plays. ''Take up the glasses of thy sight.'' Coriolanus, Act 3, Scene 2. ''I can see yet without spectacles.'' Much ado about nothing, Act 1, Scene1. ''Seek for sorrow with thy spectacles''. 2 King Henry IV, Act 5, Scene 2. ''Your eyeglass is thicker than a cuckhold's horn''. Winter's Tale, Act 1, Scene 2.

When all salient factors are analyzed, a definitive statement can be resolved to the effect that one may glean from research of the literature and other scientific evidence that the advent of spectacles dates from about 1280 A.D.

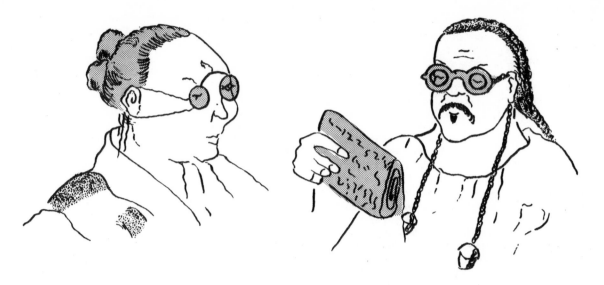

Reproduction of sketch showing ancient Chinese modality for holding spectacles in position.

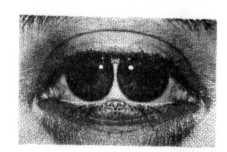

Oops!

Requires special specs.

Apologies--The Optician (British).

Dig those groovy new specs you just got!

PLATE #3

1. A methodology used as far back as early 19th century to early 20th century of testing for a usable reader. Part of the armamentum of the itinerant spectacle vendors and by jeweler-opticians. This folding set contained nine numbered foci which related to the vendors stock (see text).

2. Steel single barrel; solid nickel; trial frame. The more advanced vendor had concave lenses from 2 to 144 inch focal length. Around 1875 20 pairs of astigmatic lenses were added and an assortment of prismatic l e n s e s. These single lenses were glazed with celluloid or metal rims. Interchanging the lenses, a lengthy procedure, often resulted in some degree of accuracy of focal requirement. A set of this type sold at the time for $82.00 complete. Present day upgraded sets basically of the same principle sell for $1000.00. Smaller sets were available for the jeweler-optician.

3. More advanced trial frame; circa 1900.

4. Prospective glass: In usage middle 18th century. All mother of pearl over brass. Resembles a telescope, however, it is the prototype telescopic spectacle used for sub-normal vision correction at near point. It serves more like a monocular microscope but affords a larger reading field of vision. In France and in England an arrangement was devised for this prospect glass so that it could be used for distance for ogling the women. It was called the "lunette de jalousie" and sold at the time for as much as $4500.00. Madame de Pompadour paid 180 livres or 900 English pounds for a prospect glass. Some were decorated with gold, silver, ivory, porcelain, wedgewood, and embellished with precious stones. They were considered works of art.

5. Optometer: Nickel plated over brass; original cost $.75 each. (Patent applied for C. 1875). A reading chart was inserted in the holder opposite the eyepiece which could be moved along the rod containing etched markings for "concav" and convex for self determination of the correct lens. A substantially inaccurate method of ascertaining the focal deficiency of the eye. Nevertheless, this method or a like approach has been employed since its inception by mail-order houses for self-evaluation of the lens requirement for mail-order specs. (See glazed goods.)

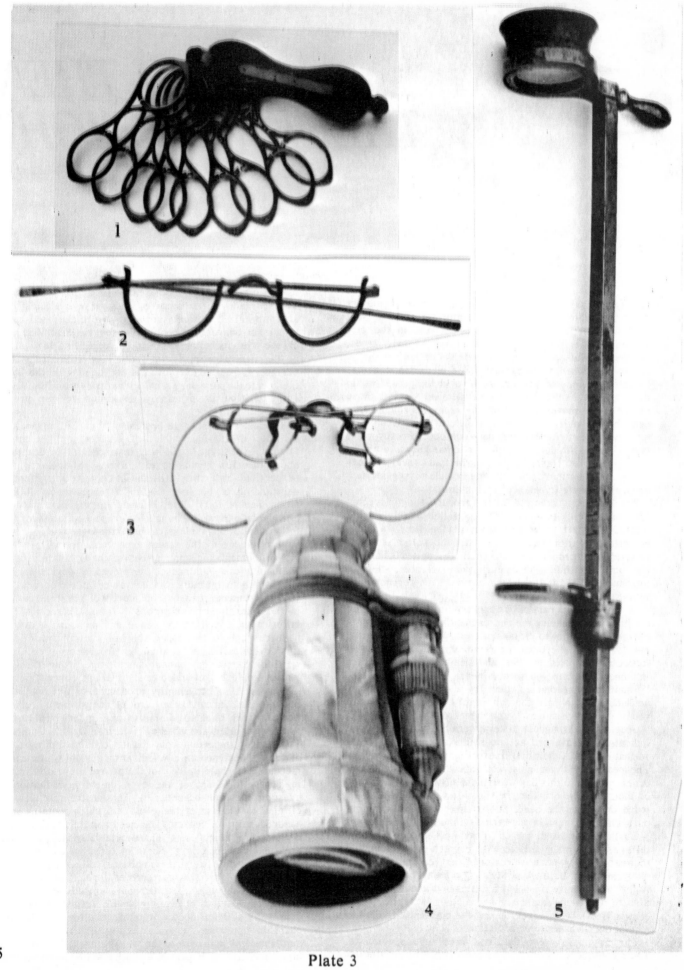

Plate 3

3 AND THEN THERE WAS LIGHT

Despite their obscure origin we can safely say that spectacles began to gain popularity about the beginning of the 14th century, first being sold by itinerant peddlers and by stallkeepers in the city arenas. These itinerant peddlers, as part of their wares, carried a trial set device of some eight or ten completed pairs of numbered spectacles*' (See plate #3) to assist in selection for the proper age level of the person whom they were to suit. The greatest demand was for those glazed with convex or magnifying lenses, which serve best for the older, and then more literate, individual who was desirous of correcting aging vision.... .Presbyopia*, vision of the fifth decade of life. Little was known of lenses for Hyperopia* (farsightedness), Myopia* (nearsightedness), Astigmatism* (corneal or lenticular irregularties) or Oculo-muscle imbalance* (prismatic).

The knowledge required for the proper fitting of spectacles was still in its infancy. The so-called *trial and error* method was all that was known at the time - a crude but effective alternative. Rarely did the *patient* succeed in selecting a proper corrective lens that suited both eyes. Not until the late 19th century were scientific methods introduced to aid in the determination of the correction of visual defects.

In the Western part of our country, in the latter part of the nineteenth century the approach to the fitting of spectacles was related to be as follows: When a prospective eyeglass wearer entered the establishment, "he would be looked over, asked his age, and then he was told to reach into one of the bins which contained a quantity of identically numbered spectacles, then try a pair from each box until he found a pair through which he could see "pretty good". The price range was anywhere from $5.00 to $200.00.

Spectacles throughout history were considered to be an indication of advanced age or that of a morbid infirmity, so that efforts at their disguise took many ingenious forms. The nearsighted who must wear spectacles constantly, in order to see, to this day wear them anywhere but in front of their eyes where they belong. Most often they can be found on top of the head, at the tip of the nose, dangling on a chain or held in the hand as a means of affectation.

On the other hand, the converse is also true. History tells us that many people with perfect eyesight prefer to wear glasses as an indication of the weakening of their eyes caused by the profound status of being a "book worm". A few will indulge in such dramatics because of their desire to hide the telltale signs of aging (wrinkles. . . . . crow's (feet), as a cover-up for the blackened area as a sign of overindulgence or addiction.

The Egyptians were the first great eye specialists. Their knowledge, however, was concerned with and limited to eye disease only. In the early 17th century, Johannes Kepler made an exhaustive study of eye ailments and also organized optical knowledge. He elaborated on the effects of convex and concave lenses. He described parts of the eye, including a statement regarding the function of the central part of the retina, and indicated that the peripheral part mainly directs the turning of the eye to the central portion which gives the sharpest vision. This function is precisely analogous to our present thinking.

Thomas Young*, a professor of physics at the Royal Institute in London, published a paper in 1799 entitled "Sound and Light." He was instrumental in developing many theories germaine to vision - particularly color perception - which is still the basis for our present understanding of how we see and interpet color. In 1856, at the age of thirty-five, Herman Ludwig Ferdinand Von Helmholtz expanded Young's color perception theory and followed with other classical breakthroughs. He increased our knowledge of the visual apparatus, specifically with his refinement and applications of the Ophthalmoscope*. Helmholtz and Kohlrausch developed a device in 1866 with which to measure the curvature of the cornea. The two instruments can be considered of greatest moment in the determination of errors of vision (refraction). The latter device lends monumental and profound knowledge with respect to the topography of the cornea. Without this device called the keratometer (from keratus, the Greek word for cornea) or ophthalmometer, the fitting of contact lenses would be relegated to a "trial and error" method.

Among the first quantity producers of fine ophthalmic instruments, around the turn of the present century, was De Zeng Standard Company of Camden, New Jersey, which was later absorbed by American Optical Company. Their most important contribution consisted of a battery of lenses designed in a wheel arrangement which can be mechanically held in front of the patient's eyes. By rotating these in front of the eyes untold combinations of prescriptions can be obtained. This instrument virtually eliminates the use of the trial set* which contains some hundred pairs of lenses. The need for the added encumbrance of a weighty and uncomfortable trial frame* also was made unnecessary. Some of these instruments are still in use and in great demand as collector's items by members of the vision-care professions. Present day instruments, serving a like purpose, embody almost all of the salient features of the original De Zeng skioptometer*.

In 1863 a Dutch doctor, Herman Snellen, developed a chart to appraise the visual acuity of his patients by a mathematical approach to the visual angle*. Variations of this chart are still part of a routine visual analysis per-

Plate 4

Two of the numerous stylings for chicken specs.

formed by vision-care specialists. The most noted early scientists whose efforts brought about practical methods of refraction* were Young*, Donders*, Helmholtz* and Gullstrand*.

Pioneer physicians knew little of optics and regarded the prescribing of glasses beneath their dignity. George Gartisch, the famous German ophthalmologist, severely condemned their use in his textbook published in 1583. Van Arlt, in the 19th century, was the first ophthalmogist of repute to pay due attention to glasses as a valuable adjunct to medical armamentum.

Conditions of life in America previous to the 18th century rendered the need for corrected vision with glasses unnecessary for the majority of individuals. In addition, as stated previously, their cost at the time was frequently prohibitive. The ability to read and write was characteristic of only the affluent and learned few.

The earliest artisans constructed the primitive spectacle by providing two pieces of leather which were fastened onto a cap worn low over the forehead. This was later followed by a looped arrangement around the ear with strings which were sometimes weighted. These held effective lenses of a sort. Early 18th century Americans made spectacles which showed evidence of the people's struggle for survival, the hardships they endured and the little time they had for the pleasanter amenities of living. Consequently, the spectacles were solid and plain, with no fancy frills. They were made strictly for a utilitarian purpose. Some early American spectacles were so crudely made that the temples show the original sawtooth marks where they were cut from a piece of sheet stock. The refinement of filing had been overlooked or omitted, in contrast to the European spectacles of the same era which were highly embellished and ornamented to the point of being garish.

Spectacles came into common usage in England about 1750. The long temples or bows* were called "telescope sides" or "turnpins" according to the mechanism by which they varied the length to fit the wearer. It was not until then that what we now know to be the prototype for today's spectacles became popular. These contained the regulation front section held in position by temples or bows. The length and type of bow was an indication of the period of popularity. Spectacles with the long, straight, solid temples were indicative of the pre-Revolutionary era and were worn by George Washington about 1769. (See Illustration).

The sequence of improvements which followed, however, was dependent mainly upon the material at hand and the available technology. Frames were fabricated at the outset, as previously mentioned, from such material as wood, horn, bone, papier mache, and during the early 18th and 19th centuries, metals which were followed by real tortoise shell at the beginning of the 20th century. Shortly after, the latter was replaced by synthetic plastics in the form of cellulose acetate, cellulose nitrate, (zylonite) nylon, plexiglas and metal frames which were produced from almost every workable metal, such as nickel-silver, iron, bronze, aluminum alloy, steel and gray metal as well as the precious metals; silver, gold and, to a very limited extent, platinum.

It may be timely here to mention that the development of plastics created a new era in frame styling. A good synthetic plastics, to be used for spectacle frames, required as much as one year to be properly seasoned to reduce stress and fully cure the polymer*. Special curing chambers are provided by the "shell*" frame manufacturer with controlled atmosphere which afford a proper curing facility. The latter is mentioned primarily to explain the scarcity of plastic (zylonite) antique frames circa early 20th century. Plastic frames became brittle and crumbled easily with age.

Until 1826 very nearly all American spectacles were imported from Europe, a practice which continued until the Civil War. Progress in the optical industry in the United States since then is legendary. The development of new optical products was almost phenomenal in nature. Such enterprising firms as American Optical, Bausch & Lomb, Shur-On and Titmus were the leaders. The men responsible for starting these establishments should be highly exalted in some optical Hall of Fame. Their precision products later far surpassed even the quality of the products of Carl Zeiss Optical of Jena, then considered the foremost in the world.

Between 1867 and 1904 innumerable variations and improvements to both the spectacle and the eyeglass poured forth from the ingenious minds of members of the growing vision-care professions. The prototype developments were of all levels covering the gamut from manufacturers to doctors, later interspersed with chic offerings from the foremost members of the designing professions, such as Christian Dior, Oleg Cassini, Pucci, Pierre Cardin and Biki of Italy, all seeking a common objective: to design a frame both stylish and comfortable, as well as functional.

During this period frames and mountings preferred both by the purveyor and the style-conscious wearer consisted of the Hoop Spring and Fingerpiece mountings which were in vogue simultaneously. The Fingerpiece was marketed several years prior to the Hoop Spring however. Later it was rightfully termed the "torture chamber*." The solid spectacle was far superior for comfort and service, particularly where strong prescriptions for high astigmatism were involved from the standpoint of proper mechanical alignment and the need for constant adjustment. The slightest maladjustment could present a serious visual problem.

In 1746 an optician named Thomin of Paris advertised glasses which "allow free breathing." This was apparently to remedy the pressure exerted on the nasal passages by the weight of the eyeglass bridge or the French counterpart, the "pince-nez".

A great stimulus to the rapid growth of the optical industry stemmed from the disclosure that the presence of Astigmatism* (Young) of the eye can be an essential cause of "eye strain." McAllister Opticians of Philadelphia were credited with being the first to grind lenses for the correction of Astigmatism. John McAllister, early in the 19th century, purchased a bushel of "specs" and started an optical firm which continued successfully for more than a hundred years in the same locale. This was the real beginning of the optical industry in this country. McAllister was a perfectionist and insistent on quality workmanship. In 1812, importation from Europe was halted because of the war. Mr. McAllister then started the manufacture of gold and silver spectacles. Similarly, compound lenses* were first ground by G.B. Airy in 1825. At about the same time, Zentmayer (also of Philadelphia) was the first dispensing optician to limit his business to the preparation of glasses in accordance with prescriptions written by doctors. Philadelphia was then a great center for optical activity; James W. Queen (1853) of that city had trained many apprentices in his Queen's Optical Company.

As stated, not until the latter half of the 19th Century was greater impetus given to the visual-care profession aided by the contributions of Helmholtz (1851)* and by Donders (1864)*. Only then could a scientific and realistic eye examination be given for the purpose of relieving suffering that resulted from infirmities of the ocular apparatus.

The optical industry in the United States made rapid progress beginning with the year 1825 and many men of ingenuity and mechanical ability were responsible for

Relating to those "good old days".

this progress. The following is a list of the more prominent Americans whose contributions should receive particular notice for their inventive abilities: Cummings of Providence, Rhode Island (1867); Prentice of New York (1867); Want of New Haven, Connecticut (1867); McDonald of Newark, New Jersey (1868); Bausch of Rochester, New York (1868); Clements (1871); Burbank of Springfield, Massachusetts (1875); Hempler of Washington (1877); McAllister of Philadelphia (1885); Gilbert of Philadelphia (1886); Peckham of Big Springs, Kansas (1886); Meyrowitz of New York (1887); Wells of New York (1888); Borsch of Chicago (1895); and the Julius King Company of Chicago. The dates indicate patent paper approval. The latter four plus J.J. Bausch of Rochester were the men whose developments were the most influential and whose companies are still in existence as dispensers or manufacturers of optical products. Others merged or were absorbed by firms of similar interests.

The optical manufacturing industry had its inception, for the most part, in New England in the small town of Southbridge, Massachusetts in 1826. Prior to this time optical frames, lenses and findings* were imported from Europe, mainly France, Germany and England. Some metal frames were also produced by local manufacturing jewelers and other metal workers. The quantity, however, was limited to private demand for singularly custom-made frames.

In 1826, William Beecher came to Southbridge, Massachusetts from Connecticut to establish a jewelry-optical manufacturing shop, having served as an apprentice in Providence, Rhode Island. The first ophthalmic articles he produced were silver spectacles which were followed by blue steel. In 1869, the Americal Optical Company was incorporated and consolidated with the holdings of William Beecher, et al. Numerous changes of principal personnel followed. The debut of a lens grinding plant in 1883 precluded the need for importation of lenses from France and Germany. Sixteen years prior to the incorporation of American Optical Company, J.J. Bausch set up an optical shop in Rochester, N.Y. which has since evolved into one of the foremost optical establishments in the world, the Bausch & Lomb Optical Company, now a public corporation.

In the Southbridge and Providence area, around the year 1830, only twenty-five or thirty men were known to be engaged in making spectacle frames from gold and silver, and some few from steel. Those first spectacle frames, made in the above-mentioned areas, were mainly the work of William Beecher, whose name was mentioned earlier. When he finished one lot he would pack the spectacles in his carpetbag and depart for Boston, specifically Washington and Bromfield Streets, where a number of opticians had located. He encountered a great deal of sales resistance in his efforts to sell these handmade frames. Prior to his introducing American-made frames, spectacle frames had been imported and cost less. With difficulty he managed to sell four dozen steel frames before returning to Southbridge. In 1850 he celebrated his then greatest success when his annual receipts rose to the unheard-of sum of $9,000.00.

On a preceding page of this book the reader will note the statement that from Mr. Beecher's beginning sprouted the vast empire of the American Optical Corporation, the largest optical conglomerate in the world, with an employment roll of 15,000, including 250 local wholesale branches. As gross annual business for 1971 is unavailable, being privileged information. Its brochure, however, indicates assets of $1.5 to $2.0 billion. Other products manufactured in the large corporate scheme of diversification consist of microscopes, ophthalmic instruments, safety equipment, medical computerized and programming instruments and professional furniture. In 1967 the company merged with Warner-Lamberts, a public

corporation, whose annual sales for 1971 (which includes those of American Optical) is rated at 1.25 billion dollars.

Mr. Edwin P. Wells*, Superintendent of the Gold Frame Department of the American Optical Company, in a talk before the New England Association of Opticians on March 18, 1896, spoke on the method of spectacle making at the time and stressed the individual worker as responsible for the production of the entire spectacle. The worker was truly the artisan and required a lengthy prior apprenticeship. The quality of the product of that time is in itself evidence of the fine workmanship of the individual craftsman.

Competition is the primary factor which brought about the changes from this so-called antediluvian method of operation. What has replaced this is the factory or industrial system controlled by computers and automation so that modern eyewear obviously shows the regimentation of being factory-robot made. Durability and individuality suffer greatly. Metal frames of the present scheme of manufacture are made to last the shortest reasonable length of time. No interest is shown in refinements of engraving or individual variation of style--one frame looks like another. They literally fall apart in time for the scheduled eye re-examination - a one, or at best two year period. No stress is put on quality, To borrow a cliche, *Things are not made like they used to be.* Lenses drop out; the metal bends easily; threads become stripped with the slightest provocation; screws break and present imminent problems in retraction; solder points are too weak; etc. These characteristics make it even more advantageous for individuals to seek out frames of past eras and re-use them - especially those produced around 1930. Competition at the time demanded improved frame technology. Even the screws had extra means to secure mechanical permanency, some protected by an additional safety capping device. (See illustration #1A).

Many of the early manufacturers of optical goods listed below have long been absorbed by or merged with socalled parent companies to a point where present day optical manufacturers are guilty of practicing monopolistic methods and have been duly reprimanded by the related governmental agency with legal confrontations and large fines. One may safely say, however, that these have made no appreciable inroad on the continued unorthodox practices nor has it affected the economy of these cartels. Following is a partial list of pioneer optical manufacturers who have been so affected: F.A. Hardy & Co., Winsted Co., Standard, E. Kirstein & Sons, Globe, Dezeng, DuPaul-Young, C.F. Merry, Providence, Geneva, Southbridge, Julius King and those snapped up of late--Shuron, Continental, Whitney, Kono, Univis and many others. The few single entrepreneurs can be finger-counted.

The formal practice of Optometry* first began in 1890, coincidently with the advent of the success of the electric light (Thomas A. Edison 1879). This latter event obviously created a great upsurge in the demand for spectacles. The incandescent lamp contributed immensely to the increase in educational demands. The improvement in lighting provided longer unusable hours for reading and writing without undue effort.

Formal dispensing of spectacles evolved from the itinerant peddlers through hardware stores and jewelry shops to optical stores and finally professional optometric offices, changing the practice from *spectacle vending* to *spectacle fitting.*

As late as 1901 the professional OPTICAL JOURNAL condemned the itinerant spectacle peddlers with the statement: ''If you value your eyesight, you will place no confidence in the statement of tramps who go from house to house selling spectacles. They will tell you your eyes are *diseased* and nothing but their *electric* or *magnetized*

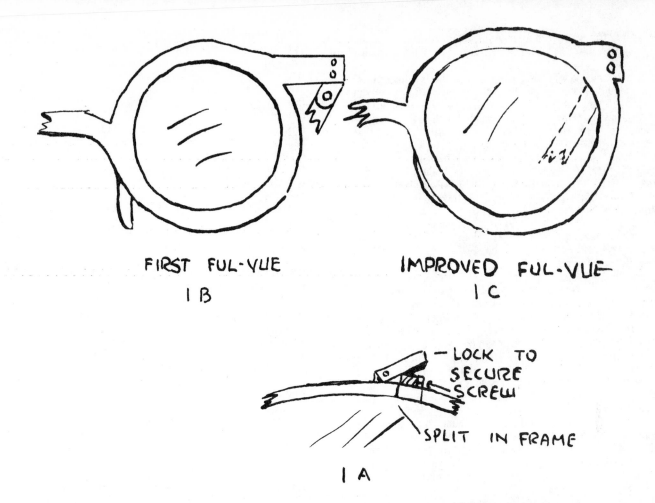

FIRST FUL-VUE
1 B

IMPROVED FUL-VUE
1 C

─ LOCK TO
SECURE
SCREW

SPLIT IN FRAME

1 A

glasses will save you from blindness''.

By the turn of the present century spectacle frames were produced in this country by a bevy of companies. Many of these are still active. The largest, of course, is American Optical followed by Bausch & Lomb, Kirstein Optical*, Titmus Optical, Virginia Optical, Univis, Optical Products Corporation, Robinson-Houchin, Continental Optical, Newport, Harlequin*, Bobrow, Stevens, Bishop, New Jersey Universal, Whitney, Kono, Bay State, Kremitz, T & P, Bechtold, Gaspari, Superloid and more. Each had their respective hallmark* inscribed on their product.

Pioneer companies like Martin Copeland of Providence, Rhode Island, who manufactured the finest solid gold vest pocket chains, lapel chains and watch fobs, turned to optical frame manufacture as a small part of their production schedule. Not until the early 20th century were ophthalmic endeavors separated from the retail jewelry trade, as with the partition of the status of barbering and human surgery. Not until 1920 did the Martin Copeland Company devote their entire production to the fabrication of the finest metal spectacle frames.

Interestingly enough, around the 1850's the gold and silver used for the manufacture of spectacle frames was obtained by melting down the fifty-cent gold pieces obtained from California and from the French crown and the Portuguese dollar. As late as 1912 one dozen ''Fine Steel Ladies' '' spectacle frames, glazed with reading lenses, sold to the retailer for $1.50. For that year the production schedule for the American Optical Company alone consisted of 50,000 dozen frames and mountings, as against 2,500 in 1882. This is an example of the extent of the demand and the rapidity of growth for this relatively new industry.

In the period following the year 1920 most metal frames were of white gold or white gold filled (1/10th 12 karat). This persisted until Bausch and Lomb and Continental

Optical advertised Pink Gold which approximated the color of the complexion of the skin. The introduction of frames in the yellow or pink cast literally replaced the popular white gold, until shell or multicolored plastics took a foothold in 1938 followed by the restrictions on metal fabrication in other than war industries. In 1966 with the advent of a new society and a return to the wires, thin metal rims and rimless, the great demand was for the yellow gold. About 1970 metal frames took on an additional color factor. Electro-deposition of a variety of colors and hues; blacks, copper, antique bronze, gun-metal gray and pewter, in the main, and a few of the primary colors especially red and blue.

About 1920 an adjunct to the metal and metal-rimless frames began to make its appearance in America. . .the introduction of genuine tortoise shell frames. The owners of the Bobrow Company of Brooklyn, New York, who manufactured tortoise shell buttons, purse frames and Spanish type decorative hair combs, were approached by their foreman, Mr. L. Grossman, with the residue of the tortoise shell after the buttons were jigged from the main shell body. He had the ingenious idea of making spectacle frames from these attached circular openings and straight pieces, thus beginning the tortoise shell frame industry. The shells removed from the tortoise were imported from Portugal and Brazil. A great deal of preliminary processing was required to make the ''shell'' pliable and workable. Many pieces were too small and/or too thin, necessitating lamination and welding with acetone as the solvent.

Some time later Mr. Grossman learned that a bank had foreclosed on Mr. Leopold Strauss, owner of the Optical Products Company of E. 16th Street, New York City, for inability to meet loan commitments. Mr. Grossman made the necessary arrangements to acquire the defunct company from the bank by satisfying the loan. Optical

31

Products Co. was later formed into a family-held corporation and became the leader in shell frame design and manufacturing.

A good percentage of the owners of the leading optical manufacturing companies presently in operation, received their primary indoctrination while working at O.P.C.*. Mr. Grossman invented and patented many optical appliances such as the "Fitover*". The author knows that American Optical Corporation at one point between 1940 and 1950 paid royalties to Mr. Grossman amounting to over $25,000.00. Other developments included the "Set and Fit" pads*, Coquette frame and heavy-weight Cardinal frame His efforts convinced the Monsanto Corporation, manufacturer of plastics, to formulate a plastic especially suitable for spectacle frames. They finally developed the cellulose nitrate compound; of late this material has been outlawed by F.D.A. because of its volatile characteristics.

Working with genuine tortoise shell presented too many problems for factory production, the most common one being that the shell cracked and crazed very easily, which triggered the need for the plastic. An interesting note is that the synthetic material resembles real tortoise shell so closely that the difference can be detected only by the antistatic test*; however, the lustre of the natural product cannot be duplicated. The cost element also made the synthetic more amenable to production. Other synthetics used to fabricate spectacle frames were acetate, methyl methacrylate, and nylon.

The use of tortoise shell and horn from which spectacle frames were fabricated existed in other countries much before the 17th century. Nevertheless its popularity become more apparent in our country because of its mass production as part of our rapidly growing optical industry.

Continuous confrontation followed between the makers of metal frames and those producing "shell" frames. The result of these disputes was not unlike the proverbial *progress syndrome* whereby a condition of rivalry followed in which newer competitive products were developed. What developed in this instance was metal-shell combination frames, Windsors*, shell eyewires* and metal centers with metal temples and ends, shelltex and the like. *A whole new line constantly showed its face.* Further application resulted in continuous creative styling of frames to insure continued wearer demand. "Shell Houses" proclaimed that their frames were superior and could be supplied in all colors of the rainbow. New departures in frame design for the "metal houses*" included regular rimless, Ful-Vue*, semi-rimless called the Numont*, Rimway*, and Wils Edge*. The shapes of lenses were more numerous than the ingenious mind could grasp.

An interesting regimen developed several years following the introduction of genuine shell frames and their counterpart synthetic zylonite frames. The temple portion was found to require a sturdy hinge to provide the durability and movement needed to serve its function. At first an all shell hinge was devised, called the split joint, which proved unsatisfactory. Then a metal hinge was developed and attached to the temple and front sides with metal rivets. These rivets were later formed into designs which were called shields and offered an indication to the origin of the frame, sort of a hall mark. For example, a V shape represented Victory Optical Company. A shield formed as an arrow was the distinctive mark of Optical Products Corporation.

The use of metal hinges attached directly to the center of the shell eye rim at the temple portion of the frame created a further problem. Because the positioning was usually at the eye-line or datum line it invariably interfered with or obliterated side or lateral vision, especially when "heavy" shell or library* temples were used. This presented a serious hazard while driving, particular-

ly when backing-up, which requires side vision. About 1931 a patent was obtained which provided for the elevation of the temple to a position considerably above the eyeline - to the top rim or thereabout. The designer approached Mr. L. Grossman of Optical Products Corporation with the design in an attempt to arrange for the manufacture of such frames. But Mr. Grossman did not agree to process this new idea, stating that he already had designed and had in production a number of Zylonite frames with the temple piece slightly elevated, namely the Mephisto and later the Coquette. The designer then contacted and interested Newport Optical Company. The result of that meeting turned out to be disastrous for both the company and the designer. The particular frame creation proved impractical and garish in appearance.

The eyerim which was designed to be round necessitated a longer extension from the upper rim, giving the frame a styling which did not command buyer appeal (see drawing B). The demand and merchandising of the frame was too limited and failure was imminent.

The American Optical Corporation later obtained exclusive rights to this patent which still had many years to run and redesigned the "Zylo" with the eyerim pear-shaped, and base of the pear being at the top of the frame. This alteration greatly improved its appearance (see drawing 1C). The extra long hinge area was eliminated leaving a small, handsome hinge in its place. The American Optical Company sponsored a nationwide advertizing campaign to the extent that all future frames of any material were considered passé unless they were Ful-Vue*, "A.O.," introduced Ful-Vue metal and rimless metal followed by top-rimmed rimless. The result of this changeover was a simple one: any manufacturer of frames wishing to remain in business had to pay tribute in the form of royalties to the American Optical Company for each frame produced where the temples were elevated above the central line. The royalty payments continued uninterrupted for about ten years. Eventually smaller manufacturers began to "bootleg" "Ful-Vue" frames. Much litigation followed, reaching a point where the American Optical Company somewhat relaxed its hold on the smaller manufacturers. A design patent is known to be legally very insecure in the policing operation.

One principal reason for the demise of the rimless spectacle when originally produced, and the rimless eyeglass of the same era, was the breakage factor. Lenses broke very easily, even with the attempted improvement of the Numont and Rimway top bar. Continuous lens breakage was costly, time consuming and often resulted in serious eye injury. When first produced the center piece was rigid. Although a flexible bridge was later substituted to minimize the stress on the lenses, this still did not solve the problem. The advent of plastic lenses within the last decade, though, has completely ameliorated this problem. Plastic lenses are impact resistant and practically unbreakable, an additional reason for the recent increase in popularity and consequent return of rimless glasses.

What was thought to be the ultimate and longest enduring frame style resulted from constant bickering between the two factions of frame manufacturers, namely the all-zylonite, heavy duty spectacle frame which made its appearance following World War II. This apparently was the closest to simulate *wearing* perfection. The entire industry produced a frame, a design of one not far removed from that of the other. Industrial espionage was rampant. In addition, a somewhat lighter weight frame (.125 Stock*), was created for women and children and in many shpaes, including the Harlequin*. These were followed by the addition of costume jeweled plaques which later became an extension of the eyewire. This continued in vogue for the better half of a century with only slight variations or improvements until the recent innovation of the thin metal rim; "wires"

Previously, style conscious spectacle wearers had demanded that their glasses be of the most inconspicuous appearance. This was presumably accomplished with metal frames or rimless mountings which supposedly blended with the facial characteristics leaving the combined general appearance altered the least. The advent of the bold or heavy "shell" frame which followed, embodied a feeling of *devil-may-care,* and the glasses were expressly designed to be so obvious an encumbrance as to portray a disoriented, inharmonious appendage. The more extreme the spectacle, the greater the apparent display of individuality.

The consideration of spectacles as a factor concerned with styling brought about extremes of eccentricities. It triggered the wearing of spectacles on any occasion without a feeling of embarrassment. People were now able to wear a device to improve their eyesight and be fashionable at the same time. Spectacles were no longer relegated to the status of being objectionable.

About 1966 another shift occurred, but this time, a rebirth, a return to relate to the eras when thin metal, rimless and aviation type goggles were the "in thing". The author touches on this attitude of the spectacle waring section of our population. The general classification for this group would be called *"Era of Groovy Glasses"*. (See chapter so headed).

About the middle of 1971 some of the adherents to the thin metal rim (wires) rebellion began to waver a little. They discovered that this type of frame was not as comfortable, sturdy or practical as the "zylo" or "tortoise." Some turned to totally rimless or semi-rimless as a solution. When these are supplied with plastic lenses, they afford a better wearing quality on many counts (see Glossary -- plastic lenses). Others turned to thin "tortoise shell," which re-entered the picture. These were extremely over-sized with deep curved lenses in shapes approaching equal dimensions for the horizontal and vertical measurements, approximating gargantuan proportions. The major demand, though, still continued to fall within the fold of the thin metal rim.

Reproduction of ancient Chinese print cartooning to use of "specs".

4

SPECTACLES
FIRST CLASSIFICATION

Throughout the history of the application of a mechanical device before the human eye, for the purpose of affording some advantage to its physiological role, the hard-core spectacle has been the uppermost. A front section held in place by two temples has been the most serviceable and staple of all varieties. The vast array of so-called improved devices may have served some temporary and timely purpose of styling or whatever; nevertheless, a return to the superiority of the spectacle was invariably imminent. The illustrations and explanatory offerings to follow will relate to the time periods of their availability and usefulness.

The spectacle happening in this country commenced with the earliest worn by the colonists in America prior to the Revolutionary Era. Practically all spectacles worn during this era were of foreign manufacture. We were as yet too immature to test our resourcefulness. The first pair shown C. pre-revolutionary and imported from London, is made of steel with solid temples, five and one-half inches long, ending in a large loop. The mechanics of construction were such that the center piece, or bridge, and temples did not perform sufficiently well to secure stability when in use. The loops supplemented this inadequacy by affording a means for the addition of a cord or ribbon which could be tied behind the head. The larger loops, if need be, could grip the skull better or be entwined in the wig when worn.

Their original cost was substantial, being sometimes as much as $200.00. Hence, only the affluent possessed such treasured appliances. Only the rich or the literate could obtain so costly a functional curio. The only marking of identification on most spectacles was a number such as 22 which served as the focal power.

The first colonist known to have worn eyeglasses was a pilgrim named Peter Brown. The year was 1620. This singular factor was considered so important as to be mentioned in the history of early Americana. There is no available record of any other spectacles being used by any of the natives, nor even the utilization of such optical aid as burning glasses. There is no word of the existence of any form of optical device in use or available in America until the advent of the aforementioned class of imported spectacles.

Plate # 5 represents a fine example of two pairs of spectacles of the Revolutionary period (1763-1765). The material of construction is unquestionably a brass-bronze alloy and hand wrought. Both are hallmarked* indicating the high esteem held by the craftsman for the excellence of his workmanship. In England the hallmark demonstrated that the applicable tax levy had been paid. The temples* are made adjustable by a rivet of like material about two-thirds its length from the front section, thereby allowing a vertical movement of the rear one-third. The purpose of this device is to allow for self-adjustment of fit behind the ears. (a) ends with a loop to serve a dual function of affording a better grip against the loose hair of the wigs worn at the time and also to provide a means whereby a thin ribbon could be threaded and tied around the outside of the wig for additional security. (b) shows a greater amount of patina which indicates that the composition of the metal is high quality silver and affected more readily by oxidation. The patina should not be removed or altered, especially with this class of collectible where present reproductions are often electro-chemically treated to add this characteristic and assure increased wearer appeal. Modern reproductions are intentionally "antiqued*" in an effort to simulate the genuine article. One cannot repeat too often that a great portion of our present society, especially the younger ethnic groups, prefer to relate to the past, even to antiqued eyewear, as part of their culture.

The lenses are of the biconvexed or flat type used primarily for the older presbyopic* person, i.e. for aging vision. The endpiece or hinged part is designed with a

Plate 5

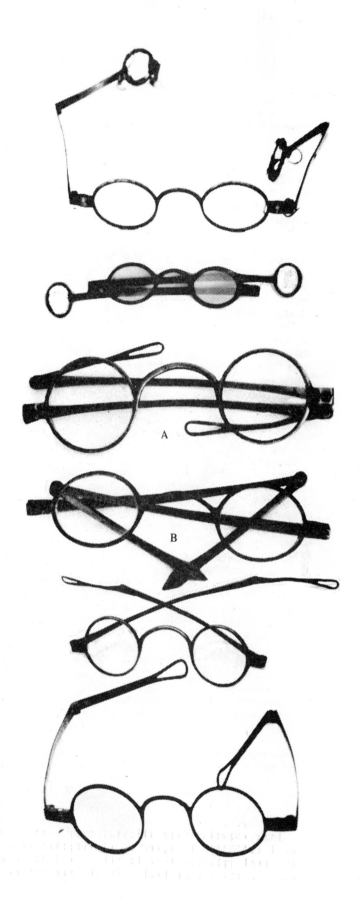

1. *Spectacles: Pre-Revolutionary, variety of largest looped temples; typical of those worn by Colonists; circa 1650. Low grade steel; heavy construction; cloth wrappings to ease pressure. First English import; type worn by Peter Brown (see text).*

2. *Spectacle: Bronze; same as #1; lenses more oval; endpiece heavier but finer construction.*

3a. *Spectacle: Pre-Revolutionary circa; solid bridge typical of era; folded on turnpin which also served to alter temple length. Most lenses of this circa were round and the product of the naturally mined mineral forms such as beryl, pebble (sections of quarts) or any emerald and topaz. The length and method of folding the temples serves additionally as an indication of circa.*

3b. *Spectacle: Same circa as #3a; probably Britania Silver discernable by hardness factor and deep patina. Had to be made heavy because this metal is very soft. Same crude construction; temple ends ends in points.*

4. *Spectacle: Bronze; same circa; showing temples opened to full length; loops smaller; this also signified later circa; same crude construction.*

5. *Spectacle: Bronze; same as #1 but smaller loops.*

Note: Aluminum alloy frame (alumnico) were first made in 1825. First major aluminum plant established 1859 in France. All other metals used for frames date back centuries. Bronze--3000 B.C. Iron--1100 B.C. Steel was made in small quantities before Christ. Since then methods date from the blast furnace method of 1340. In 1856, Bessemer in England and in 1860 Lauth in Pittsburgh refined the ancient processes. Spectacle frames of iron, steel, or steel alloy were made even before a better metal like bronze was employed. Of course, gold and silver had their day.

35

split to permit separation needed to insert the lens. This split is held together with a flat-screw. The endpiece also holds the temple in place with a rivet that allows it to swing. The method of providing a stop for the temple so that it does not swing too far away from the head and thereby fall away is particularly interesting. It is the same method employed at present by optical frame manufacturers in Great Britain, the Max Weisman Organization being the foremost. The lens* is ground and polished showing a good quality surface. The edges and shape, however, are crudely performed, obviously hand cut and bevelled. The outer flat of the temple near the hinge is stamped with the number 20 indicating its focal length to be 20" or, in our present system, plus 2.00 diopters*; accordingly, these would be helpful for near work for those between ages 50 and 55 (Donder's Table) considering that no distant visual error existed.

It is the author's professional opinion that these spectacles are still functional as simple reading glasses. A finely made metal spectacle frame is equal in construction to a fine piece of jewelry and its life expectancy is unlimited. Notwithstanding their rarity, a few are held by private collectors and a few may still be found in antique shops or their counterpart.

The specimen illustrated in this plate is in excellent condition and very rare. Nevertheless, a numbered few may still be found. The reader must keep in mind that only very few colonists required the aid of "specs."

In these writings the reader will observe that the greatest stress is placed on the consideration of the maturation of the spectacle form because it represents the overall major unit of eyewear – the mainstay – and dates back to antiquity or to the spurious inception of this bountiful device which corrects faulty vision.

Beginning with the first pair of spectacles worn by colonist Peter Brown (1620) and termed pre-revolutionary, (and assessed as the prototype Americana), the evolution, construction, mechanics and appearance can be identified by specific changes incident with the passing of time. These endeavors or improvements serve to date the specimens, should it be required for the purpose of cataloguing. They follow:

Pre-Revolutionary (1620-1738)

This period of over a century encompassed the most insignificant alterations. The distinguishing feature however, (see plate #5) consisted of temple lengths of approximately four inches, folded vertically on a turnpin arrangement and ended in a large loop. The eyerim diameter was 28 millimeters and round shaped. No provision was made for adjustment of the width between lens centers (interpupillary distance*). The material was steel. A short time later the temples were changed to fold horizontally on a hinge type construction with the loops being reduced somewhat. (See plate #5)

Revolutionary Era (1776)

The temples were changed to a sliding type (see plate #9). The method was that of a stud on one part of the temple which moved into a slot on the other part. The ring loops at the end of the temple were slightly reduced in size.

War of 1812 (1812-1820)

This era embraced the McAllister of Philadelphia inception when the sliding temples with elongated loops afforded much easier manipulation with the wig. These were also made of steel by Brewer of Philadelphia. The frames were heavy and bulky. A short time later the gauge and size of the loop was reduced. Another somewhat later pioneer, F. Dorhe (1850) of Philadelphia, made his contribution in a frame prototype which was considerably lighter in weight and thickness, with the temple loops much small-

er. The large loops of the pre-revolutionary era were found to be less functional. The stud-slit temple mechanism was also eliminated, adding a tone of refinement to the spectacle. (See plate #10)

The next change in construction allowed for alterations in the bridge by the addition of a straight extension from either side of the curvature of the bridge which was attached to the nasal portion of the eyewire. This improvement was accompanied by a return of the vertical moving turnpin of the temples. (See plate #10)

Civil War Era (1865)

This period brought with it the greatest modifications. The temples were solid and straight with no loops. The eyerims produced by the newly established manufacturing companies, such as American Optical and Bausch & Lomb, were in such assorted shapes as ovals (plate #6) rectangles, hexagonals, and octagonals. The purely round frames were non-existent at the time, having become extinct at the onset of the Revolutionary War and being followed by ovals which continued to the Civil War.

The foregoing represents the researched consecutive sequence of the earlier classes of spectacles. The ostentatious philosophical and sociological impact which these frames had on our community has been dealt with in another section of this book.

Prior to this stage of evolution, the spectacle was produced with the primary concern being its usefulness. At this point the setting changed. Designers presented frames for their principal functional worth, but great importance was given to comfort, styling and correctness of optical mechanics. This is clearly shown in the following list of classifications:

Concise Listing of Styles
in Glasses Since 1865

1865-1900 Indian Wars	Pince-Nez 0-00-000 eye blue steel frames 0-00-000 eye gold filled*
World War I 1910-1916	Finger-piece mtgs. with reels & hairpin chain Oxfords 0-00-000 eye frames in best quality gold filled PL 38 B
Post World War I 1916-1921	1/5-14K bridge, 1/10-14K, etc. All zyl frames Gold spectaclewear White gold
1926-1930	Introduction of arch bridge, zyl nose pad spectacles
Pre-World War II	Beginning of white Gold Filled
1930-1936	Ful-Vue Frames and Rimless
1936-1938	Wils Edge Various semi-rimless constructions
World War II 1939 1946	Harlequin shapes in zyl Numont Combination Frames

*Note: Gold filled frames of optical quality were not produced until 1900, notwithstanding that the alloy was first discovered in 1817 by John Turner in England. 0-00-000 referred to the size and shape of the thin oval frame circa 1890-1914. They were called ought, double ought and triple ought eye frames.

Plate 6

1. *Spectacle: Revolutionary circa; inscribed on inner face of right temple H. Sargeant, Springfield, Mass. The N is reversed. Outer face of right temple imprinted with number 10 indicating a 4" focal length. Heavy weight; thin flat temples 5/16" width; sliding temples on loop and stud arranged on silver.*

2. *Spectacle: Post-Revolutionary; brass; all looped temples; circa 1820; change from round or oval to octagon; heavy construction; first addition of extension on bridge to allow for adjustments to pupillary measurement; lenses still flat; only marking is number 22, the focus.*

3. *Spectacle: Silver; refinement of thickness and construction; endpiece still bulky; number 18 or 2 1/4" focal length; flat pebble lenses.*

4. *Spectacle: Bronze; endpiece thicker; number 8 or 5" focal length; no other markings.*

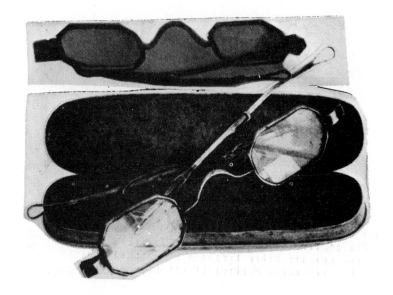

5. *Spectacle: Solid gold; greater refinement apparent; case, steel lined in velvet; similar cases being used for novelty imports of "readers".*

Plate 7

Spectacle: Post-Revolutionary; looped but more refined; lessening of frame weight and improvement of construction; no markings except for number 16 or 2 1/2'' focal length; circa 1830; all sliding temples; material ranging from brass to silver; showing varied shapes; rebirth in present modes.

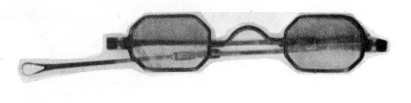

Plate 8

Spectacles: Post-Revolutionary; the center piece or bridge were called by the letter "x" or "k" or the term Liebold. These provided two points of attachment to each eyewire affording a more rigid front to the frame. These styles very costly to manufacture and hence higher in price.

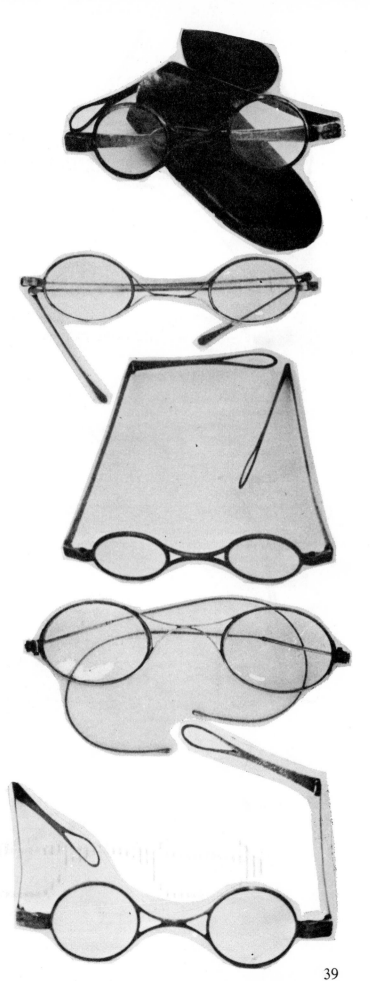

1. *Spectacle: Prototype; very heavy construction of silver; circa 1790. Case of steel with hinged cover.*

2. *Spectacle: Fine solid gold; very thin wire; excellent construction; turnpin temples; obviously worn constantly; lenses of weak power; loops gone; circa 1830.*

3. *Spectacle: Same as #1 but earlier date; circa 1800.*

4. *Spectacle: Same as #2, fine gold; circa 1860; showing wire riding bow temples; bridge left much to be wanted; temples improved wearing quality of frame.*

5. *Spectacle: Same as #1 in silver; lenses round; temples fold horizontally; hallmarked with an "S" indicating British silver and manufacture.*

Plate 9

(All photos this plate at Smithsonian Institution.)

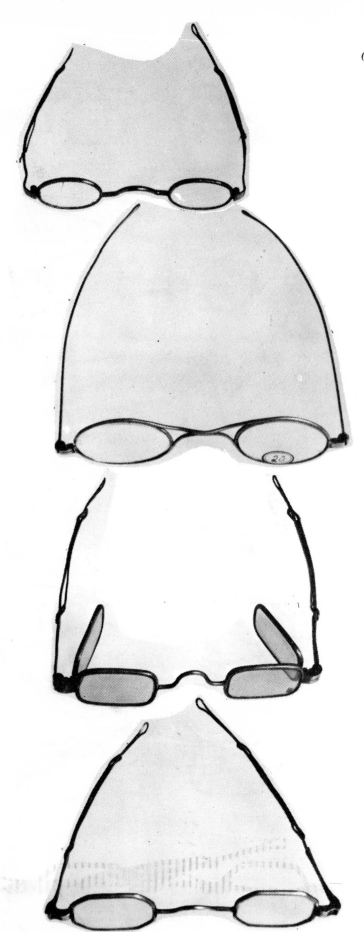

1. Spectacle, bronze frame, straight bows, box joint style, dated CA. 1400 A.D. German reading glasses.'' (Smithsonian obvious miscalculation.) Author estimated correct date to be not earlier than the turn of the nineteenth century. . .A definitive example of existing misconception of judgement of origin.

2. Spectacle: Nickel plated frames; flat tapered with enlarged "K" type bridge; oval lenses; dated circa 1850.

3. Spectacle: Brass frames; sliding extension temples; blue oblong lenses with second hinged blue lens on each side marked "Sweizer"; dated circa 1860. (See plate 10, 4th pair from top.)

4. Spectacle: Silver frame; sliding extension temples; octagon lenses, undated. Author's estimated date, circa early 19th century.

Plate 10

1. *Spectacle: Octagon; sliding temples and small oval loops; silver; lenses tinted Rose #3. Must have been glazed at a later date than of the frame because lenses were for correction of nearsightedness and astigmatism (see text) while marking on temple indicated "readers #22". Frame circa 1830; lenses circa 1920.*

2. *Spectacle: Octagon; sliding temples with small oval loops; excellent condition; "reader #16"; circa 1830.*

3. *Spectacle: Rectangle; sliding temples with small oval loops; bronze; "readers #20"; circa 1800.*

4. *Spectacle: Rectangle; sliding temples with small oval loops; brass; marking on left temple "SCHRIED KNECHT". This was prototype bifocal; second hinged lens used for secondary focus; often used as sunglass; circa 1820.*

5. *Spectacle: Rectangle; silver bridge; bronze eyewire; sliding temples unmarked; circa 1800.*

6. *Spectacle: Octagon; sliding temples with small oval loops; "Readers #10".*

Plate 11

ALL PRE-CIVIL WAR

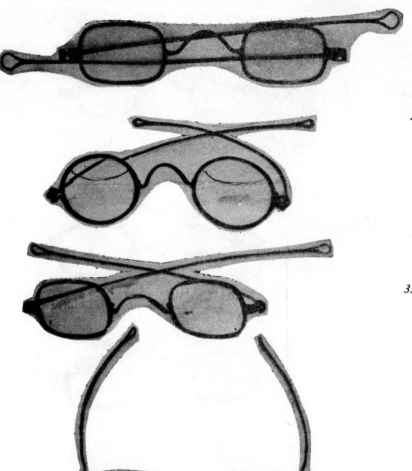

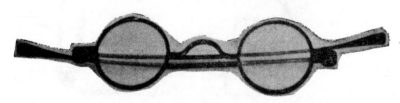

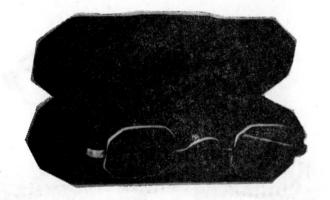

1. *Spectacle: Rectangle; steel black; beginning of thinner rim; refinement; loops smaller; circa 1850.*

2. *Spectacle: Oval; mass produced; hinge and temple clamped together by pressure rather than screwed; no split in endpiece; lenses were held together by pressure of blue steel; lenses are first form of ground bifocals; one piece of glass, two separate grindings; prototype of "one piece bifocal"; circa 1860.*

3. *Spectacle: Rectangle; silver; straight temples; smallest loops; fine construction; "reader #26"; circa 1855.*

4. *Spectacle: Same as #3 but circa 1810 (War of 1812); bridge construction poorer.*

5. *Spectacle: Round; bolder construction; no loops; bridge poor; unmarked; of bronze; circa 1865.*

6. *Spectacle: Octagon; solid gold; short temples looped; case of gutta percha; looked and shaped like small coffin; circa 1865.*

Plate 12

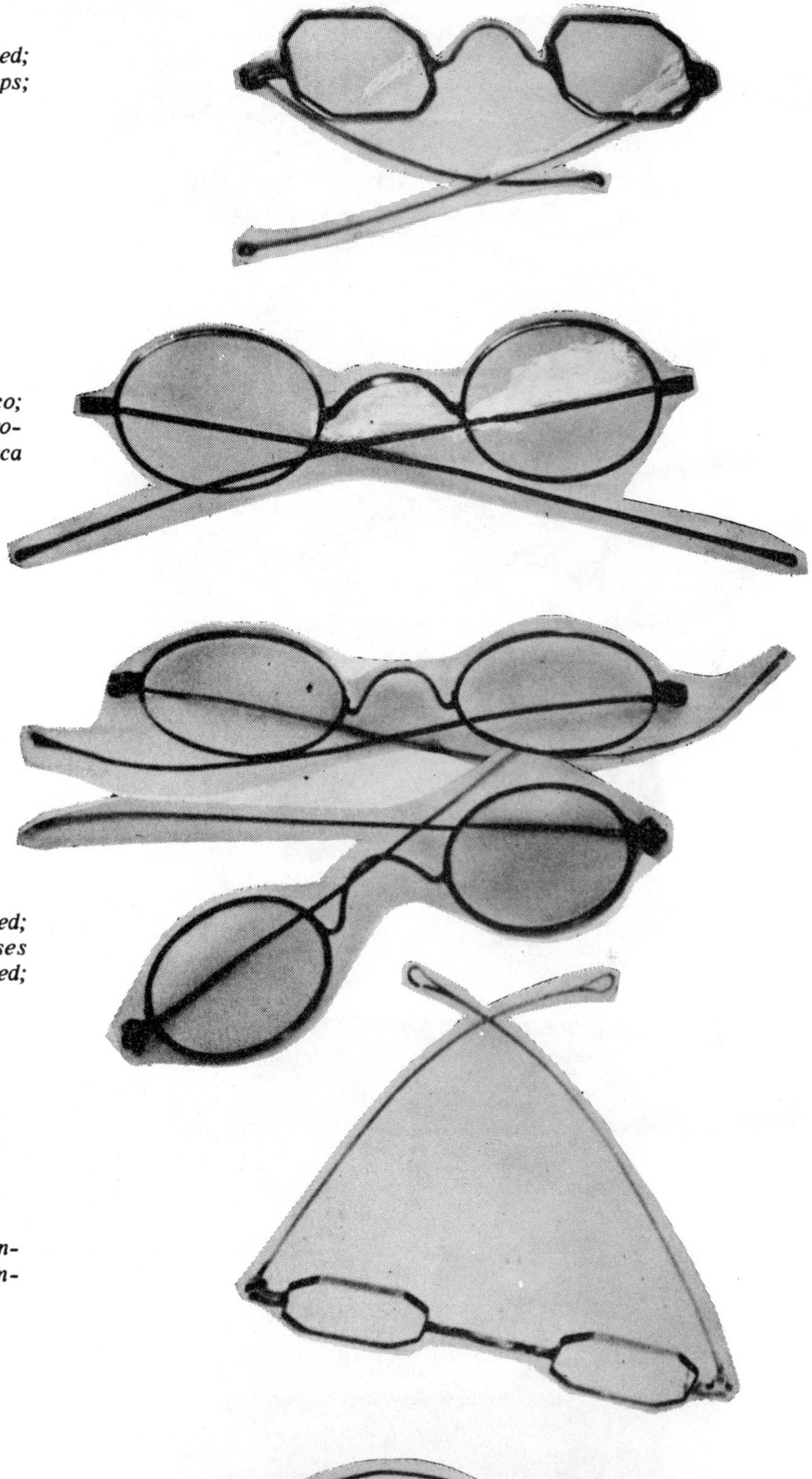

1. *Spectacle: Octagon; silver; thin-rimmed; straight solid temples; smallest loops; circa 1885--Post-Civil War.*

2. *Spectacle: Oval; nickle silver or alumnico; American Optical; straight types; produced in large quantities (see text). Circa 1900.*

3. *Spectacle: Same but solid gold.*

4. *Spectacle: Oval; steel; mass produced; reader straight temples; rims held lenses by pressure only; no screws were used; circa 1900.*

5. *Spectacle: Octagon; solid gold; fine construction; very thin metal; looped temples; circa 1880.*

6. *Spectacle: Oval; same as #2 but blue steel.*

Plate 13.

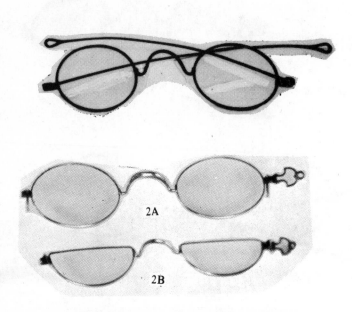

1. *Spectacle: Most common variety; mass produced; circa 1900, Pre-World War I; American Optical Co., catalogue 1912; illustrates numerous forms in all available metals; 8KT to 14KT solid gold, gold filled, coin silver, steel, alumnico, alumnica, regaloid, Roman alloy; over 200 different bridge measurements; 7 different eye or lens size and a host of temple lengths and types; straight, comfort cable, riding bow most abundant. The Spencer catalogue which predates the A.O. by 35 years shows 57 different bridge sizes. It also includes genuine turtle shell. This company was later absorbed by the A.O.*

2. *Grab front and back: Two types; employed mainly as a "piggy back" addition to #1. A) Covered entire lens. B) Worked like a half eye bifocal permitting the subject to see both for distance and near; circa 1900.*

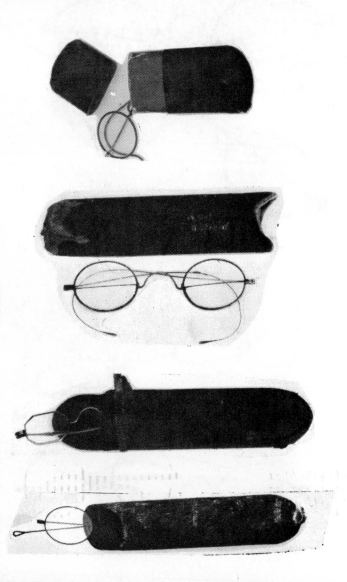

3. *Spectacle: Innerim with paper case; frame circa 1920; case circa 1850; called telescopic.*

4. *Spectacle: Replica of bifocal specs worn by Ben Franklin although frame is of a later date, like 1850; case same circa; material of case, paper. Original owner, deceased eye doctor, claims authenticity of specimen. Author questions this because of circa of frame.*

5. *Spectacle: Solid gold; circa 1860; case, paper mache; illustrated in Spencer catalogue, page 69, #258; circa 1870.*

6. *Spectacle: Steel looped temple, circa 1860; case, paper mache, circa 1870.*

Plate 14

1. *Spectacle: Skeleton; frameless/rimless; solid yellow gold; bridge flexible, called Revluc; rocking pads and later Wandonian for Wall and Ochs (Philadalphia); temples half riding bow; circa Pre-World War I (1900). This model was popular for half a century.*

2. *Spectacle: Thin wire alumnico with full riding bow temples; circa 1900.*

3. *Spectacle: Skeleton; saddle "SS" bridge; full riding bow temples; lenses are encircled by a thin "shell" rim to add additional support and improve cosmetic appearance; popular from 1914 to 1945; having rebirth at present.*

4. *Spectacle: Same as #2 with "clingswell" flexible interchangeable bridge allowed for variety of bridge sizes to accommodate different nose widths; bridge usually 10KT solid white gold; other parts thin white gold filled; temples, comfort cable; circa 1930. (See repro of adv).*

5. *Spectacle: Same as #3 but "shell" covered bridge; designed to reduce nasal pressure; modern rimless has overcome this hardship with plastic lenses which are both impact resistant and one-half weight of glass lenses.*

6. *Spectacle: All metal; usually gold filled but fully covered with hard rubber or zylonite; temples, comfort cable; this pre-empted the "tortoise shell" frame; circa Post-World War I.*

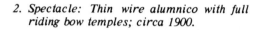

Another CLINGSWELL *innovation*

◆ ◆ ◆

CLINGSWELL, acknowledged leader in the field of rimless, owes much of its continued success to the fact that it has constantly been kept up to date, the while it has retained basic features which only Clingswell can offer.

The Gothic spring; 14 karat gold Velva Pads; delicate engraving; and a lightweight frame model, are among the successive innovations which have won countless friends for this popular eyewear style.

And now Clingswell adds another feature which is bound to meet the favor of the ever increasing numbers turning to rimless—the Grayton Guard.

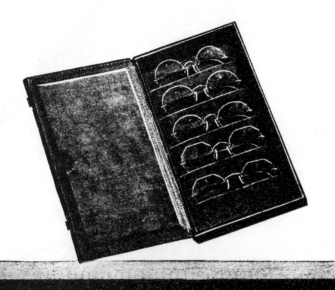

This Filling Set features Gothic Clingswell with Grayton Guards; 14 k. solid gold bridge and gold filled temples—an ideal combination where economy is desired.

The cost is so little and its use so effective that we recommend you send for a new set to replace any that may be showing the wear of constant use.

BAUSCH & LOMB OPTICAL

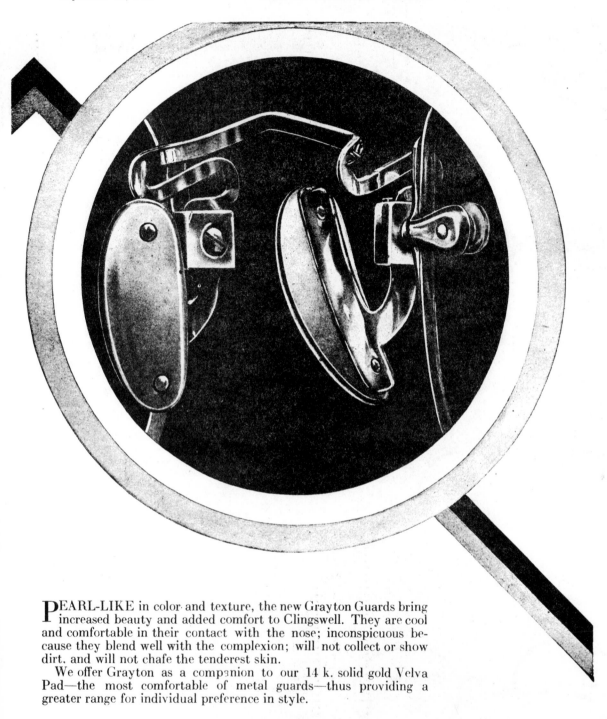

PEARL-LIKE in color and texture, the new Grayton Guards bring increased beauty and added comfort to Clingswell. They are cool and comfortable in their contact with the nose; inconspicuous because they blend well with the complexion; will not collect or show dirt, and will not chafe the tenderest skin.

We offer Grayton as a companion to our 14 k. solid gold Velva Pad—the most comfortable of metal guards—thus providing a greater range for individual preference in style.

COMPANY, ROCHESTER, N. Y.

Plate 15

1. *Spectacle: Innerim variety; demi-blonde colored zylonite covering; gold filled chassis; popular; circa 1925.*

2. *Spectacle: Half eye; all gold filled; mass produced as early as circa 1825; saddle bridge; comfort cable temples worn below the margin of the lower lid; still in vogue.*

3. *Spectacle: Skeleton mounting; saddle bridge; comfort cable temples; circa 1900; popular to the present as "groovy specs".*

4. *Spectacle: Innerim; bridge Wandonian type with metal movable pads designed for increased comfort; very popular in East (Philadelphia). Circa 1930; antidated; padded metal; thin rimmed; keyhole bridge frames. (See Olympian adv.)*

Plate 16

Sketch of Harold Clayton Lloyd (1894-1970). Famous for horn rimmed glasses as trademark. Circa 1920.

1. *Spectacle: Split joint variety; predated metal hinge; first made in celluloid, then genuine shell, and now in a variety of plastics, nitrates, (now prohibited by F.D.A.), acetates, nylons, and of late, epoxies; saddle bridge; circa 1920; presently returning in popularity.*
2. *Spectacle: Metal hinged zylonite (nitrate); saddle bridge; colors were black, mottled brown, verdal, flesh and demi-blonde, and demi-amber; circa 1930; manufactured by O.P.C.*
3. *Spectacle: Same as #2 but keyhole type bridge and stationary side pads.*

4. *Spectacle: Zylonite improved ful-vue worn to present date; circa 1935.*

5. *Spectacle: Same as #3 but oxford type; bridge variation. (O.P.C.)*

Note: Later models were like the Harlequin, octagon, oval, square, rectangle, and many free-formed shapes and a host of designer-oriented colors.

The New Yorker "C"

An exceedingly popular style because of its graceful, becoming Gothic Shaped Bridge.

Properly proportioned pads assure correct fitting and complete comfort.

Order a sample from your wholesaler.

She Wears the New Yorker "C"

FLATTERING EYEWEAR

For reading, office, sports, bridge and college

The New Yorker

One of this year's "best sellers"

Its well designed bridge and properly proportioned pads bring attractiveness and comfort to the wearer and satisfaction to the fitter.

Order a sample from your wholesaler.

She Wears the New Yorker

These flattering fashions in frames are created by

OPTICAL PRODUCTS CORPORATION

43 West 16th Street   New York, N. Y.

By the Way—Would You Mind Mentioning the Weekly? Thanks.

50

The Fifth Avenue

The combination of a lustrous, graceful 1/10-12 karat white gold filled engraved bridge with the comfort of perfect fitting zylonite pads and thin wire-cored temples.

Order a Fifth Avenue Sample Set for $8.85

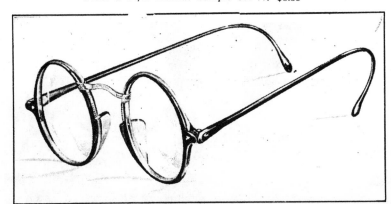

She Wears the Fifth Avenue

Four High Bridge Styles to Suit Their Features

In a variety of colors to suit their complexions

She Wears the Manhattan

The Manhattan

This smartly styled octagon top frame with gothic shaped bridge accommodates drop, leaf and fancy shaped lenses.

You can obtain two samples and a clever display stand by ordering a "Manhattan Display Set." All for $5.00.

These flattering fashions in frames are created by

OPTICAL PRODUCTS CORPORATION

43 West 16th Street   New York, N. Y.

By the Way—Would You Mind Mentioning the Weekly? Thanks.

51

CORTLAND

E7461-14KW heavyweight frame, E7351-14KW, lightweight frame (lightweight above.)

E7461-14 KW, heavyweight frame,
E7351-14 KW, lightweight frame, (lightweight above).   With their smart engraving, these frames are attractive. The heavy weight for those who like it; the lightweight particularly for women.   Both numbers are available plain.

Dispensing Solid Gold through the A O Solid Gold Plan hardly requires as an investment any more than your time and attention. The keynote of this plan is the Solid Gold Fitting Set. In this set, you may now have our 14K Cortland line if you desire it.

By purchasing one of these sets, you arc able to fit and demonstrate our entire 14K line. This is the only stock you need. Your actual orders will be filled through your A O Branch on a 24-hour Rx basis. It is easily seen that the sale of only a few pairs of 14K frames will pay for the cost of the fitting set.

Surely, the opportunity to handle quality optical products under such a proposition as the A O Solid Gold Plan is worth investigating.

E7498¾-14KW. CORTLAND ENGRAVED SPECTACLE MOUNTING. *Also furnished without the engraving. This style is very popular with business and professional men.*

AMERICAN

By the Way—Would You Mind Mentioning the Weekly? Thanks.

52

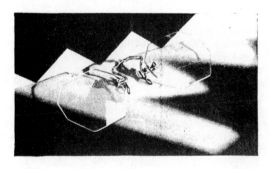

5

EYEGLASSES

SECOND CLASSIFICATION

he first means of lens adaptation before the eye for the purpose of improving the visual acuity was the quizzer. It only required a simple step further to alter and improve the device to serve both eyes. By building a small extension to two monocular quizzers and joining these with a rivet, a binocular device is obtained which can either be held before both eyes from above or below or, with some small pressure, by the nose alone. The first such dual lens system has been attributed to the ingenuity of the early Chinese.

In America the first known eyeglass to be constructed was concerned with and revolved about the work of J. J. Bausch*. His autobiography states that he found a piece of hard rubber in the street. It appeared to him that this material would lend itself well to the making of eyeglasses. He obtained exclusive rights from the rubber producers for its use for eyeglass production. Sales were poor at the very beginning. However, with the beginning of the Civil War, importation of foreign "glazed goods" again halted abruptly. This embargo served as a great impetus to the sale of rubbermade eyeglasses. This situation helped tremendously to establish the Bausch & Lomb Optical Company.

In the early 20th century the rage at Vassar, the all girls college, was the adornment of hoop spring eyeglasses, and in Harvard almost all the students donned them. Apparent-

ly an expression of station or stature . . . . . an affectation.

The eyeglass was produced in many forms. The variables mainly involved the construction of the pads which came in direct contact with the structure of the nose and there exerted a holding pressure. This pressure was often intolerable, and so, many patents were granted for the related resolution of this inclemency. Pads with the bare metal in contact with the nose, and in numerous designs in the form of shell covered, cork covered, or rubber covered pads were guaranteed to ease the "torture chamber effect"; all to little avail. Thin ribbons, cords, and light-weight chains were added as a security measure against accidental dislodgement of the eyeglass. These ended around the neck, as an ear loop or hairpin for the ladies.

The Ketcham and McDougal Company devised a patented reel which could be clipped to the waist or dress or attached to the lapel of a coatjacket. This reel performed in an ingenious way by retracting not unlike a window shade.

The composition of the eyewire or rims covered the entire gamut--"shell", metal and rimless. Provision was made for the cord or chain in the form of a loop or in the rimless, a drilled hole in the glass.

Both the factor of the uncomfortable fit and the potential lens breakage served ultimately to exclude this form from its continued usage. However, they were actively in vogue for close to a century. C. 1840-1930.

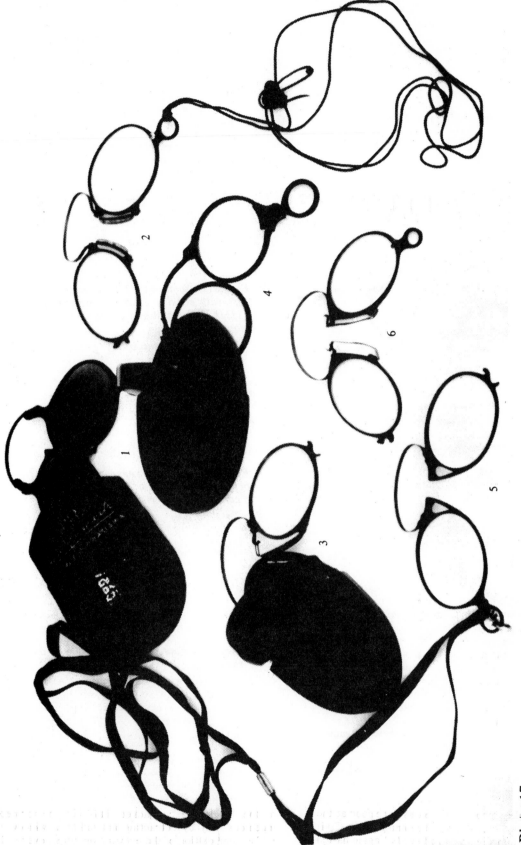

Plate 17

All circa Pre-Civil War.

1. *Eyeglass: With case hard black rubber; Bausch and Lomb; folding variety glazed with coquille; sunglasses; spring, blue steel; case, pinseal leather.*
2. *Eyeglass: Same but later model with cork pads; silk cord ending in eyeglass hook (pin).*
3. *Eyeglass: Same; pads shell; hard steel case.*
4. *Oxford: Prototype oxford (varsity). All hard rubber except steel coil springs; hard case.*
5. *Eyeglass: All hard rubber with blue steel spring with black ribbon and silver slide.*
6. *Eyeglass: Same as #3 but thin metal movable pads; all popular; circa 1860.*

Plate 18

1. *Eyeglass: Bar spring case in sized A,D, F,L; latter sometimes known as Farley bar spring; never very popular because of poor mechanics; circa 1900.*

2. *Eyeglass: Some as #1 but longer width bar, with rocking guards or pads; model #833 A.O.C. catalogue dated 1900; metal mostly solid gold.*

3. *Eyeglass: Model of present rebirth of #2 being imported from France and making a comeback; gold plated.*

4. *Eyeglass: Same as #3 but free-formed shape.*

5. *Eyeglass: Same as #3 but updated rectangle.*

Plate 19

1. *Eyeglass: Common mass-produced variety in round and oval shapes made of alumnico and extensively in use; A.O. gold filled.*

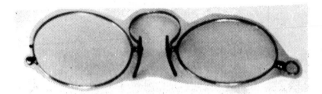

2. *Eyeglass: Same as #1, plate 18, but rimless with hole in right lens for cord; never successful.*

3. *Eyeglass: Same as #2 but framed.*

4. *Eyeglass: More recent type 1930 used as a "reader" and sold "over the counter". (See glazed goods). All parts were pressure assembled rather than with screws. More recently sold in five and dime stores for upward of $1.00.*

5. *Eyeglass: With short sidepieces called "grab butts", designed to stabilize the the horizontal movement of the eyeglass; solid gold and rare; circa 1830; used until early 20th century.*

Plate 20

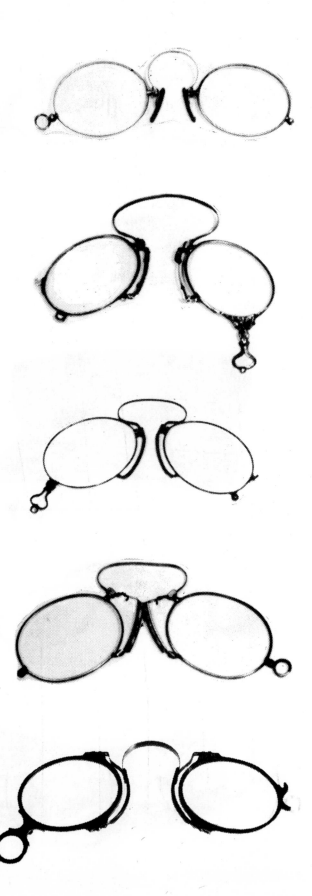

1. *Eyeglass: Solid gold; fixed pads; model #1367 A.O. catalogue; circa 1900; all parts interchangeable; specimen has shell pads, also made in alumnico and silver.*

2. *Eyeglass: Solid gold; made in 8KT, 10KT, 14KT; also in V wire with assorted handles; many beautifully hand engraved; many folding into a pendant; the 14KT solid gold glazed original, Spencer catalogue price from $27.00 to $60.00 per dozen; present value $35.00 to $75.00 each; circa 1870.*

3. *Eyeglass: Same as #2; cork nose pads and adjustable; thinner construction; Spencer catalogued price from $22.00 to $66.00 per dozen; glazed with "readers" lenses.*

4. *Eyeglass: Solid gold; non-folding; cork pads; larger "hoop" spring meant to distribute pressure more evenly; circa 1900.*

5. *Eyeglass: Pince-Nez; hard rubber frame; steel bridge; oval lenses; circa 1850. (Photo at Smithsonian Institution).*

Plate 21

1. *Eyeglass: Rimless; parts interchangeable; solid gold spring only; hole in right lens to accommodate thin eyeglass cord; circa 1860.*

2. *Eyeglass: Metal rims; alumnico; interchangeable parts; circa 1890.*

3. *Eyeglass: Bridge clamped to demi-amber zylonite rims; 100 lbs. weight; metal parts interchangeable; rims heated to expand and permit insertion of lenses then cooled quickly to contract and hold lenses firmly in bevel of "zylo"; lenses were also beveled; circa 1925 (Pre-World War II); very popular.*

4. *Eyeglass: Same as Plate 22 but narrow bridge caused by longer studs between bridge and eyewire. The studs were thus variable in an effort to accommodate different pupillary widths and nasal structure.*

5. *Eyeglass: Same as #2 but blue steel with loop arrangement to allow for cord or ribbon. Prototype of color plating of metal frames. Black, antique bronze, pewter, antique gray, etc.*

Plate 22

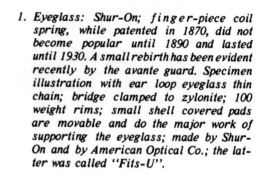

1. *Eyeglass: Shur-On; finger-piece coil spring, while patented in 1870, did not become popular until 1890 and lasted until 1930. A small rebirth has been evident recently by the avante guard. Specimen illustration with ear loop eyeglass thin chain; bridge clamped to zylonite; 100 weight rims; small shell covered pads are movable and do the major work of supporting the eyeglass; made by Shur-On and by American Optical Co.; the latter was called "Fits-U".*

2. *Eyeglass: Same as #1 but white gold filled with metal rims, same circa.*

3. *Eyeglass: Same as #1 but rimless lenses held by very thin dark zylonite rims for added security and possibly improved appearance.*

4. *Eyeglass: Same as #2 but stylized key-hole bridge; solid engraved white gold; circa 1930.*

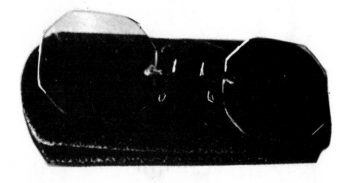

5. *Eyeglass: Rimless octagon with cortland solid gold bridge (see adv.); case "frog mouth" type.*

Caricature of Sir David Lloyd George; original pacifist changed to a staunch supporter of war against Germany; circa 1914; known for his frequent references to his finger-piece mounting.

6A

LORGNETTES

THIRD CLASSIFICATION

Plate #23 illustrates the first form of decorative eyewear. These were the prototype for the more modern lorgnette.

This plate is concerned with the most decorative lorgnettes, which were made by French and German artisans. These foreign products are discussed here because of their historical value. They were used in this country quite extensively by those of the higher social echelon as a symbol of their elevated station during the middle of the 18th century, a custom which has survived to this day. The American-made lorgnette was more functional. Its beauty was expressed in the fine craftsmanship and the high quality of metal used, primarily sterling silver and solid gold. The term "lorgnette" is a misnomer. It comes from the French and means *opera glass*. The correct term, which has never been in common usage, is *lorgnon*.

Lorgnettes were designed in many interesting forms in order to intrigue the buyer in search of decorative eyewear. Most lorgnettes were used as pendants in addition to serving the primary purpose of improving vision. Without hesitation, the author claims that more than a few hung suspended from the neck and served no utilitarian purpose, but were merely decorative. Within the past few years pendants of many facades have been worn by both male and female as a form of symbolism embracing many causes. Among these were included single lens pendants which could serve only infrequently as a magnifier for the youth so attuned.

The illustrated lorgnette on plate #29 is of unusual design. The antique shop from where it was purchased claimed it to be very rare and over a hundred years old. This was not refuted; on the other hand, it cannot possibly be more than forty years old since the V-shaped eyewire construction was not prominent until that period and an analysis of other markings clearly indicated the later time. The dispensing price at the moment of manufacture could not have very well exceeded $35.00; its present asking price is $125.00 and the metal is only semi-precious silver. Quality of workmanship also leaves much to be desired.

Quality lorgnettes in gold, shell and silver were first made in the United States in 1896 at 15 Maiden Lane, New York, by Spencer Optical Co. (See plate #25). Spencer later turned to making the finest microscopes in the world. The company was absorbed by American Optical who began producing the microscope and other scientific optical appliances and instruments. The prototype lorgnette made in France was called in the latter part of the 18th century, the "Binocle d'Incroyable."

Plate 23

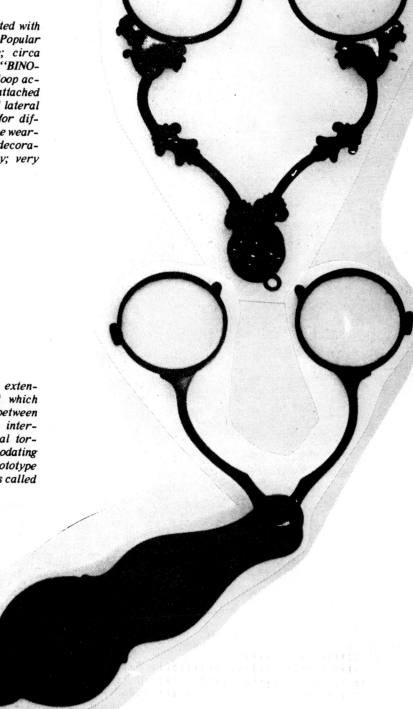

1. *Lorgnette: Silver; highly ornamented with much face and animal symbolism. Popular in France under Le Directoire; circa 1750; called scissors-glasses and "BINOCLE d' INCROYABLE"; bottom loop accommodated ribbon or chain and attached to the mechanism which permitted lateral movement of lenses to account for difference in pupillary distances of the wearer and also to fold. Prototype of decorative lorgnette popular to this day; very rare.*

2. *Lorgnette: Silver lens rims and extensions ending in an arrangement which allows for change of distance between them to account for variances in interpupillary distances. Handle of real tortoise shell with space for accommodating lenses when folded; circa 1820; prototype of American lorgnettes; sometimes called "wishbone" lorgnette; very rare.*

Plate 24

1. *Lorgnette: Pure amber throughout; rare; belonged to Duchess of Luxembourg; circa 1856; handmade; note cherub holding loop for chain or ribbon; folding.*

2. *Lorgnette: All high quality; 18KT solid gold; handmade; unusual designed openwork with no mechanical springs or catches; folding; circa 1890; hallmarked Geo. C. Shreve & Co.; has several file marks used when acid tested for gold content.*

3. *Lorgnette: All real (genuine) tortoise shell. Circa 1875; all hand wrought; shown in Spencer Catalogue to sell to retailer for $3.00 each. Also made in calluloid at $1.50 to $5.00. Present value $250.00.*

4. *Lorgnette: Same as #3; reinforced with sterling silver band; original cost $3.00; circa 1875.*

5. *Lorgnette: Presented to writer by the family of Mack Sennett of comedy fame; chain loop also device to hold lenses in place when closed; circa 1875; genuine shell; all openwork.*

6. *Lorgnette: Genuine shell; same as #3; circa 1875.*

7. *Lorgnette: Zytonite black; folding variety; more recent version; studded with marcasites (common variety of iron pyrites); used extensively in costume jewelry and carried over to decorate spectacles; circa 1950; later changed to aurora borealis, synthetic gem stones which were made by a deposition of magnesium fluoride coating onto glass.*

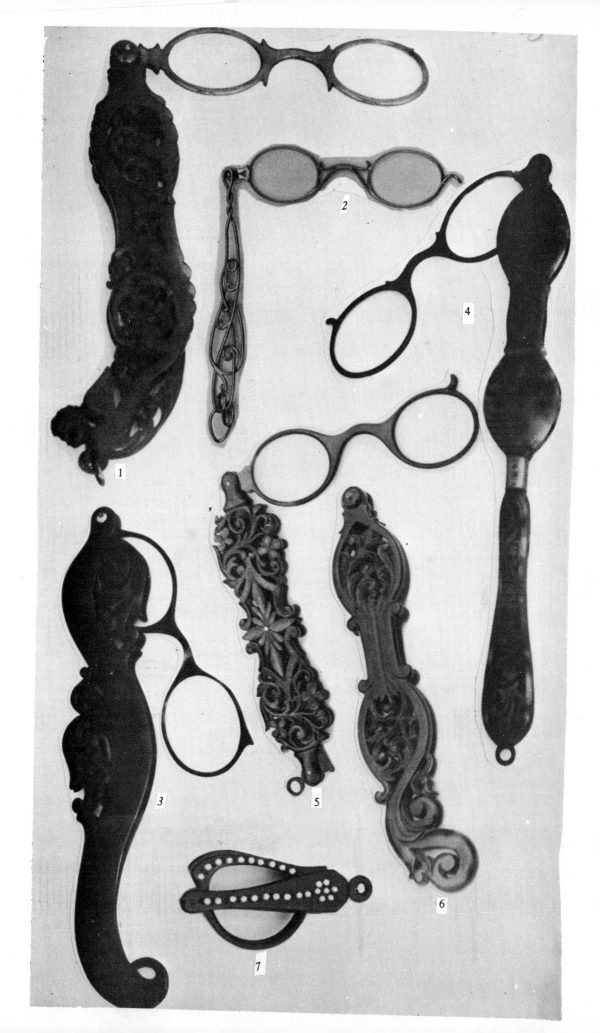

PLATE #24

65

Plate 25

1. *Lorgnette: Pressed steel or tin plated black; studded with seed pearls; common variety; circa 1900; many manufactured by Spencer Optical Co.*

2. *Lorgnette: Same as #1 but gold plated and different motif; circa 1900.*

3. *Lorgnette: Solid gold hand-engraved; originally called eyeglass; folding variety; catalogue price circa 1875, per dozen, 10KT $72.00 to $96.00, 14KT $84.00 to $108.00, 18KT $108.00 to $144.00. Present value $200.00 each.*

4. *Lorgnette: British silver with black enamel decor; button on handle releases catch for opening; hallmarked with anchor of Birmingham assay office; circa 1850.*

5. *Lorgnette: Iridium platinum studded with gem quality blue-white diamonds totalling 3.3 karat which include those in satoir chain. Custom-made as an ensemble; individually serial numbered 7073 for insurance purposes; octagon-shaped; folds into a beautiful pendant glazed with flat Kryptok prescription bifocals; circa 1910; present value $3500.00.*

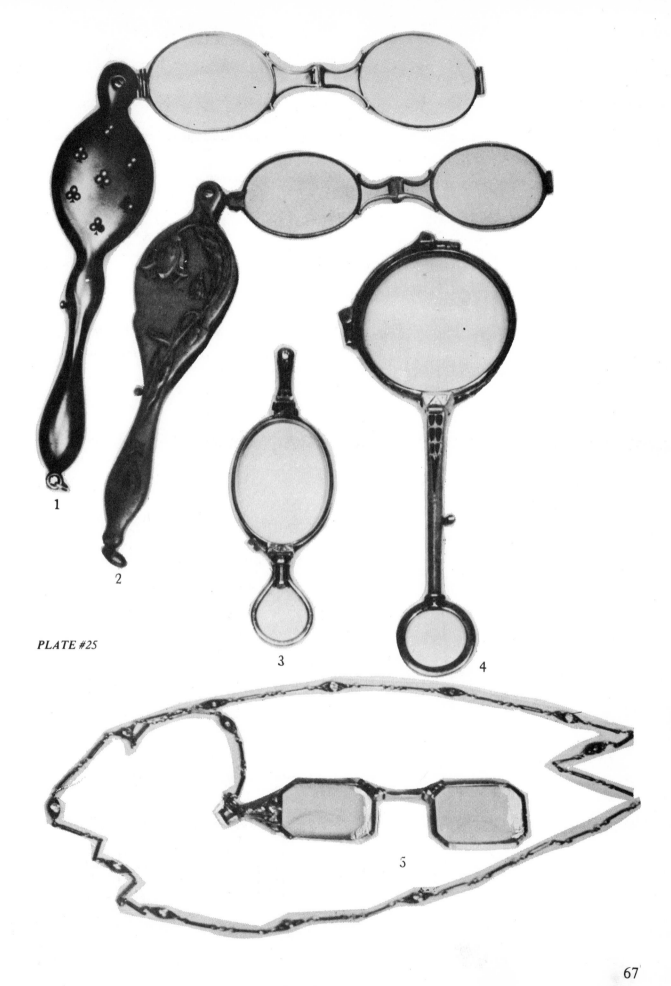

PLATE #25

1

2

3

4

5

67

Plate 26

1. *Lorgnette: Handmade by Louis Grossman of O.P.C.; genuine tortoise shell; unique; only one made; circa 1920; similar models made by Spencer; priced $3.50 to $6.50; now value is $150.00.*

2. *Lorgnette: Silver eyerims and spring; handle genuine tortoise shell; circa 1910; unique.*

3. *Lorgnette: Long handle like French type but American made. Gold plated on silver; three rings near end loop move along handle and spring release lens rims to open; circa 1920.*

4. *Lorgnette: Same as #3 of Plate 25; open view.*

PLATE #26

2

3

1

4

69

Plate 27

1. *Lorgnette and chain interspersed with black beads; silver plated openwork black nickle; circa 1860; beautiful specimen; present value $200.00.*

2 thru 6. *Lorgnette variations of product of Spencer Optical Co. Made in gold, silver, gold-plated on silver, gold-plated bronze, and pressed steel. Name of recipient often engraved on front of casing. Many were worn as ornaments without focal power (afocal). Original cost in 18KT $27.00 to $48.00 each according to weight.*

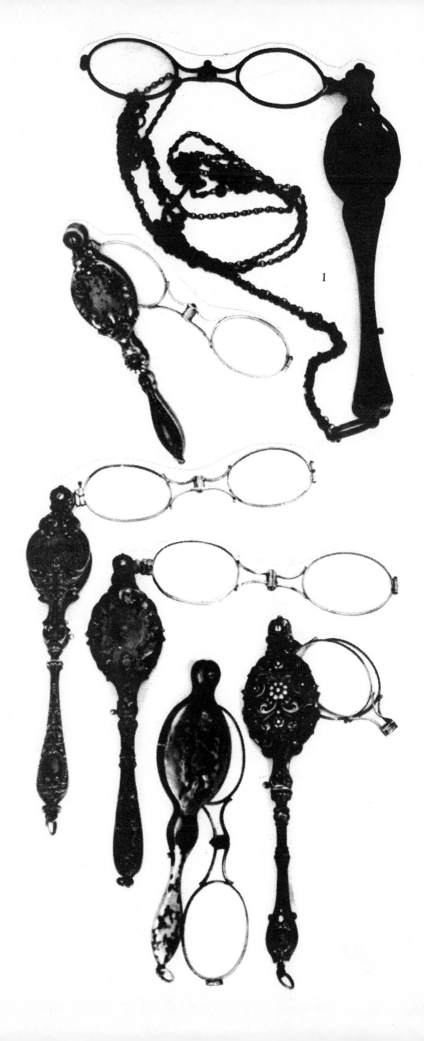

PLATE #27

1

Plate 28

1. *Lorgnette: Stainless steel with pinseal leather case attached as part of ensemble; hallmarked ZOCHER D.R.P.; obviously Pre-World War II; circa 1930; in gem condition.*

2. *Lorgnette: Solid gold with silver chain; highly decorated handle; black onyx stones and diamonds; circa 1900; quite unique.*

3. *Lorgnette: 14Kt solid yellow gold long handle worn by owner for many years as evidenced by wear marks on loop were chain rubbed constantly; circa 1890; present value $450.00.*

4. *Lorgnette: Iridium platinum; same make and design as Plate 25, item #5; less diamonds; silk cord held together with platinum slide cord shows considerable wear; circa 1910; present value $400.00.*

PLATE #28

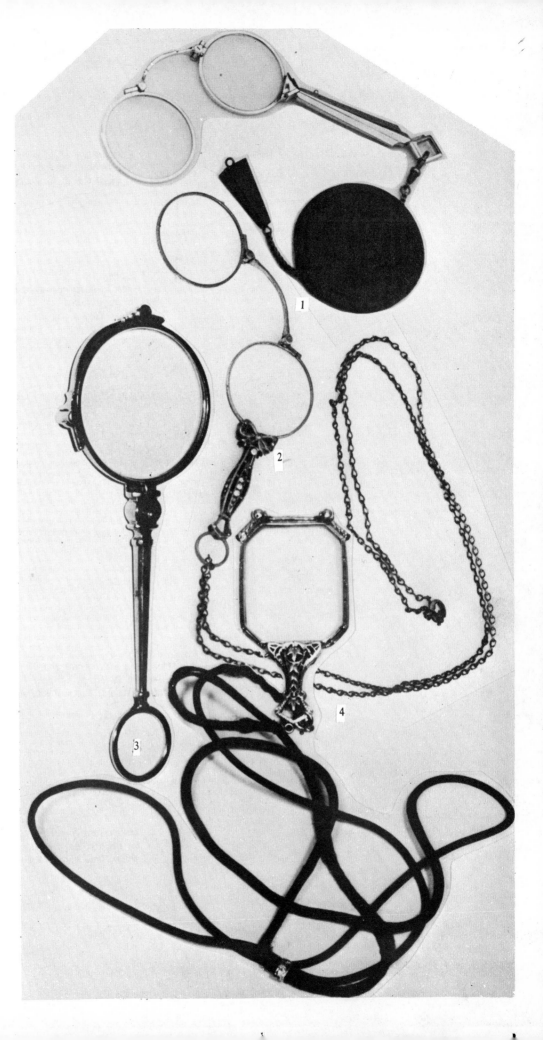

Plate 29

1. *Lorgnette: 1/10 12KT yellow gold filled subtle hand engraving; manufactured C&H Optical Co. of New York City; circa 1930.*

2. *Lorgnette: Solid yellow gold; stamped 14KT; hand engraved openwork (filigree); manufactured by G & W Optical Co. of New York City; circa 1930; present value $250.00.*

3. *Lorgnette: Sterling silver; machine engraved; folding; made by famous T & P Optical Co. of New York City; circa 1930.*

4. *Lorgnette: Solid yellow gold, 14Kt; circa 1900; non-engraved (plain).*

5. *Lorgnette: Solid white gold; 14KT marked on catch which released lenses; beautifully hand-engraved; circa 1900; (shown in open position).*

6. *Lorgnette: Novelty type silver; referred to in text as misquoted with respect to circa; true circa 1930.*

PLATE #29

75

Plate 30

1. *Lorgnette: Small edition; genuine tortoise shell casing; hung on chain as a charm but functional; sterling silver eyerims; circa 1920.*

2 & 3. *Lorgnettes: Small edition; genuine mother-of-pearl eyerims; gold plated base metal; circa 1920.*

4. *Lorgnette: Closed view of Plate 28, item #6.*

5. *Oxford: White gold filled, 1/10 12KT Schwab guards; American Optical; circa 1932. Introduced as a result of constant breakage factor of standard folding oxford spring. Made only with pear-shaped lenses called P3. (P for pear and 3 the mm difference between horizontal and vertical measurement.) More practical than conventional type. Only improvement in oxfords since original circa 1830.*

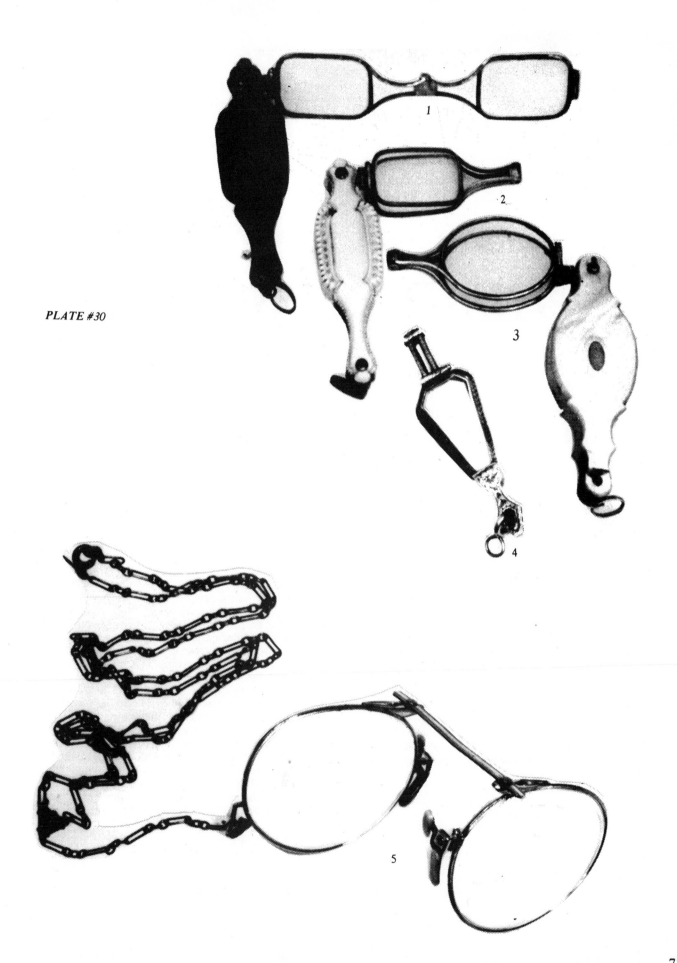

PLATE #30

6B

OXFORDS

THIRD CLASSIFICATION

Oxfords, both folding and non-folding, have been in common usage continually since the early forms worn by the Chinese, Italians and French. The old "Pince Nez," the French term for the eyeglass type of eyewear, was the prototype for the more modern oxford which was so popular around 1920 and thereafter, and is now making a great comeback. Some models of the "Pince Nez" were made in a folding style, probably to prevent damage by minimizing the exposed area. Later improvements were tastefully designed to enhance their appearance and to simulate a pendant or charm.

The oxford both non-folding and folding was first manufactured in our country around the turn of the present century. They were produced at the onset by American Optical Company (called Varsity), Krementz, and Tried and Proved Optical Company. These companies used precious metals in their scheme of developing the sales potential of this product. It was their thought that the more affluent would be in the market for such an unusual and novel visual device. A little later on all-shell oxford was produced by Bausch and Lomb followed by shell rims and metal spring by Optical Products Corporation.

The prototype oxfords in metal worn with a black ribbon were meant for the men. However, when the shell oxfords came into vogue, men quickly changed to the more masculine appearing shell. The women, on the other hand, preferred the metals. Some metal oxfords were produced in platinum and profusely studded with diamonds. The satoir chain attached to it also was embellished with diamonds.

Obviously, such show of splendor is wholly reserved for evening wear. The writer has in his collection a magnificent pair whose present value is $3,000.00. It contains 3.3 karats of pure white diamonds. It required a bit of haggling before he persuaded the auctioneer to let him have it. It may be of interest to note that catalogue #9 of the Spencer Optical Manufacturing Company issued about 1880, contained no display of oxfords of any kind while a number of highly decorated lorgnettes and folding eyeglasses were illustrated and listed. This company at the time was known to produce a complete line of lenses and frames.

At this point it may be timely to explain that people who are hampered by aging vision (presbyopia – a gradual loss of the near-point accommodative faculty) require the aid of glasses only for near work, the distant vision being normal. It then follows that glasses need be worn only when the individual is engaged in near work like reading, writing, sewing and any other occupation where near point acumen is essential. The visual appliance, therefore, can be such where an oxford affords a constant and convenient availability to the near lenses, serving at the same time as a finely appointed ornament.

In recent years even the regular types of spectacles have been suspended and held by a thin black cord or chain so that when the near glasses are not in use they can be allowed to dangle from the neck, thus being held in readiness by this simple scheme. The reader should keep in mind that glasses for near vision cannot be worn constantly since their stronger focus blurs distant vision, necessitating their removal when not worn for their intended purpose.

Plate 31

1. *Oxford: Combination zylonite eyerims and metal spring and guards; Product of O.P.C.; circa 1925; folding variety; very impractical but quite ostentatious.*

2. *Oxford: White-gold filled 1/10 12KT most common variety worn mainly by the feminine both as a visual aid and as an affectation; made by Krementz of New York City whose wares were of the finest; folding variety; circa 1930.*

3. *Oxford: Solid white-gold 14KT; non-folding variety; manufactured by T & P (Tried and Proved); all hand-engraved; a fine specimen; the guards were of the Schwab variety. Dr. Schwab was an ingenious optometrist of Atlanta, Georgia. This guard made it possible to use the oxford for constant wear; circa 1930.*

4. *Oxford: 10KT solid gold with chain and Ketham and MacDougal reel; regular guards; hand-engraved product of American Optical Co.; circa 1920; referred to in the text as an unusual recent purchase at Devonshire Downs, Reseda, California.*

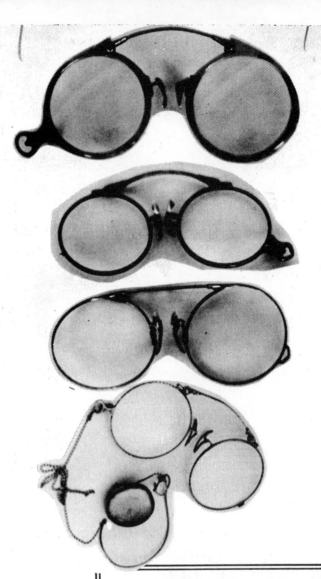

ADVERTISEMENT: Bobrow Optical Co.; dated 1928.

Plate 32

1. Oxford: White-gold filled with stream-lined spring and Schwab guards; 14KT solid spring only; folding variety; small button on handle serves to activate catch when folded; manufactured by T & P; circa 1935.

2. Oxford: Same as #1; different handle.

3. Oxford: Non-folding variety; 10KT solid white-gold; regular guards; extremely light weight for continuous wear; circa 1930.

4. Oxford: Same as #3 but with replaceable spring which often broke on all oxfords; Schwab guards.

5. Oxford: Same as #3 but with Schwab guards.

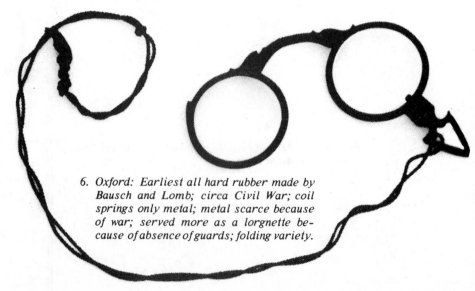

6. Oxford: Earliest all hard rubber made by Bausch and Lomb; circa Civil War; coil springs only metal; metal scarce because of war; served more as a lorgnette because of absence of guards; folding variety.

PLATE #32

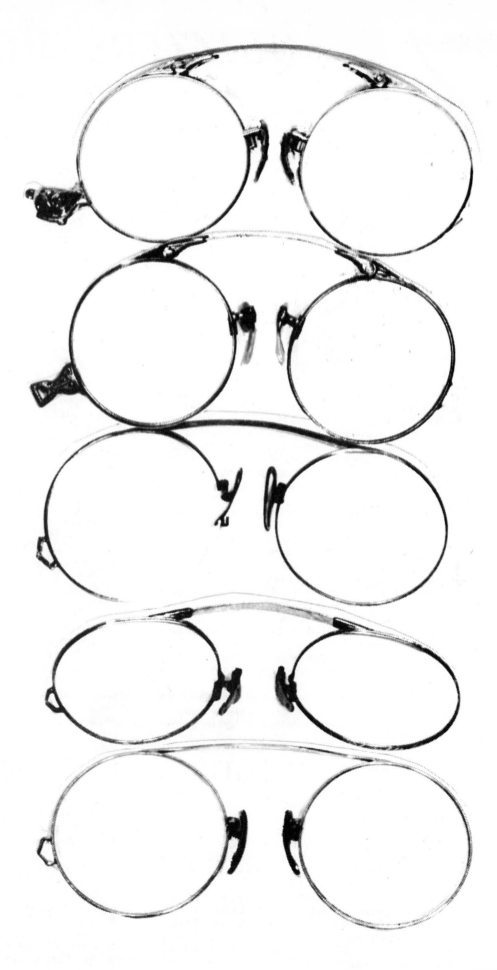

7 QUIZZERS, MONOCLES, MAGNIFIERS

FOURTH CLASSIFICATION

late #33 illustrates a number of monocular visual devices which were in use from the middle 18th to the 19th centuries, such as the (a) hand magnifier, (b) Quizzer and (c) Monocle. The hand magnifier is little different from our present version except for some small refinement. The one illustrated is the product of American Optical Company, circa 1910, and constructed of solid, gold non-engraved. The handle is in the form of a loop and offers a means to add a chain or thin cord which will permit it to dangle from the neck. It is used mainly for magnification purposes rather than ophthalmic.

The quizzer, as has been stated, antedated the dual lens spectacle. In fact, prior to the 18th century it was called a spectacle, with the dual lens spectacle resulting from the single lens being joined with a pin to another single lens so that they could either be held or clipped onto the nose to serve both eyes. It is usually held by hand at some distance from the eye and closer to the person or object to be viewed. During the period when it was in vogue it was made in many designs in metal and highly ornamented. During the 19th century no male would be seen without a quizzer suspended from his neck at the Royal Court or other formal social occasions. When held in front of one eye it appeared to add a touch of drama to an occasion. In more than a few instances the sight advantage gained by peering through the quizzer was questionable or nonexistent. Its purpose was not unlike the kerchief of yore which adorned formal attire "more *show* than *blow*." In early periods, quizzers were made so that the framework embodied a key for winding the wearer's watch. The present day hand-held magnifier is an offshoot of the quizzer.

The engraved quizzers illustrated on plate #33 were all foreign made. A. is made of silver circa 1780 (Charles X). The large loop is affixed on a swivel arrangement, possibly for doodling or to minimize tangling. In B. the lens is "plano" (of plain glass), while all the others have a focal point for extremely short range (4" to 6" from the viewing object). C. is oval of a somewhat later vintage and more ornate, A. and B. are of circa 1915 and resemble the small magnifiers of today.

The monocle played an important role in Central European countries during the period between 1807 and 1910, when it was at its peak and extends even to the present. Its use was especially prevalent in the Germanic countries. Many monocles have extensions in the form of thin metal projections called gallaries which serve to engage the upper and lower folds of the loose areas of both lids and is thus embedded so that stability of position is maintained. It is comfortable and is framed with a thin metal rim usually constructed either of thin non-engraved but knurled metal or with no metal framing or projection, but in rimless form. The edge of the all glass monocle is knurled to provide a better anchoring facility. Provision is made for a thin cord either in the drilling of a hole in the all-glass monocle or by a loop in the frame. The monocle was first advertised by Jones Brothers in England in 1813. It made its appearance more emphatically at the Vienna Congress of 1814-1815.

To reiterate, the monocle is always round and is held in place in front of the eye, above by the brow muscles and below by the muscles of the cheek at the lower lid border. It is worn mainly by men. However some daring women have been known to have succumbed to this form of eye device. This may be considered an early expression of *women's liberation*.

Although the monocle had its inception about 1807, its origin is still speculative. It has been thought to have had its beginning as a prop in a stage play and from this pretentious cradle it was adopted by the British aristrocracy as an effective indication of station.

The evolution is as follows: The quizzer followed the primitive reading glass held near the object, later the glass was held before the eye with the hand, then the monocle was used being held in place by the muscles of the brow and, again the quizzer was an outgrowth of the monocle with an extension for a handle.

When one considers the rarity of one defective eye when the mate is normal, it follows that the use of this device must be an affectation rather than purposeful.

Several of the chapters that follow will include subject-matter relevant to "Specs" but more concerned with their general application. The author is a practicing optometrist **and** feels this to be representative of important reader appeal. His column "Dr. Eye" appears in every issue of a Los Angeles, California newspaper. It is of the question and answer variety. These chapters will relate to those questions most frequently asked. The doctor is in the midst of completing a manuscript he calls "The Sight Scene" which is a compilation of the questions and their answers, including an in-depth discussion of present day vision-care.

Plate 33

1. *Quizzer: a,b,c, earliest type; circa 1780; French (King Charles); prototype of modern magnifier. (See text.)*

2. *Quizzer: a) Chinese; metal rim and trim silver; handle jade; used mainly as a magnifier; circa 1830. b) Metal silver; handle ornate enameling; circa 1780. c) Same as (a); circa 1810.*

3. *Quizzer: a) Bronze; circa 1750; used in New York. b) 10KT solid gold non-engraved; used mainly as a magnifier; manufactured by American Optical Co.; tubular gold construction; fine craftsmanship; circa 1910; also called Amoptiscope (American Optical); was also made in rimless; specimen shown in catalogue page 138 as item #1952; made in foci of 3'', 4'', 5'', 6''; supplied with flexible leather button flap case. (See text.) c) Same as (b) but folding; of smaller diameter and made of alumnico; circa 1910; replica in present use and quite popular. (Vest pocket size.)*

Old sketch ridiculing use of monocle.

1805

 Old sketch illustrating a proper stance for the use of a quizzer.

Steel case holding quizzer shown above and to left.

1

2

Sketch of George Arliss (1868-1946). Actor who achieved fame for his vivid and convincing characterization of historical figures. Most famous for portrayal of Disraeli who was identified by his monocle.

Plate 34

1. *Monocle: With extensions called gallaries; yellow solid gold; circa 1815; knurled edges.*
2. *Monocle: With gallary forming a loose spring ending in loops, When tension is released, gripping quality is greatly improved; circa 1900.*
3. *Monocle: Yellow gold filled; same as #1 but smooth edges; loops provided for thin ribbon.*

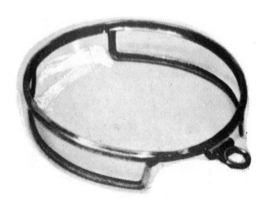

3

8

ABOUT SAFETY LENSES

T̸he incident of eye injury in American industry and in other forms of endeavor such as sports, travel and the military is staggering. Employees engaged in both hazardous and non-hazardous occupations are open targets. Blind institutes have estimated that such accidental occurrences number 100,000 annually with five percent of these losing their eyesight either partially or totally.

Within the past decade there has been a concerted effort to minimize this unnecessary waste by the use of protective eyewear. Many states have passed legislation requiring the use of safety goggles when encountering potential imperilment. Legislation has been effected in most states making it obligatory to wear safety goggles when so engaged. Within the past two years some states have made it mandatory that safety lenses be prescribed by the vision specialists for all individuals under eighteen years of age as well as for those employees who work in potentially hazardous occupations, such as hospital attendants, policemen, firemen, and other law enforcement officials; including a limited group whose one eye is non-functional. Effective at the beginning of 1972, all prescription lenses and sunglass lenses, wherever dispensed throughout the United States, are required to be subjected to an impact resistant* process which must meet government standards for safety in accordance with regulations propounded by the Food and Drug Administration and the Bureau of Standards. Safety prescription lenses can be provided in two minimum thicknesses-either 3.1 millimeter to meet industrial specification or 2.2 millimeter for dress use or everyday wear. The new organic plastic lenses made mainly of Columbia Resin 39* is considered equal to shatterproof. Plate #35 illustrates some early and some more recent safety goggles worn in industry and during hazardous activity.

Reprints of articles related to safety lenses appear on several of the following pages. Namely: "Chemically Tempered Ophthalmic Lenses" and "A New Plastic Lens". These were featured articles in professional journals and were written by the author. They are representative of historial and factual information. Their relevance will become obvious as the message they provide will be readily comprehended.

CHEMICALLY TEMPERED OPHTHALMIC LENSES

Almost six months have elapsed since a decisive and restrictive stipulation was imposed upon the spectacle wearing community at the doctor level by the FDA* carrying with it severe penalties for the violator.

The ruling of the commissioner relative to IRL*, although confusing in several of its tenets especially with respect to its application to the ultimate consumer or doctor-patient confrontation, is generally understood and easily made operative. However, there exists a number of inequities which are obviously both unreasonable and unscientific.

The **Federal Register** indicates that as a result of additional inquiries and comments received from representatives of the ophthalmic community and the consumer community, the commissioner has con-

*IRL . . . Impact Resistant Lenses
*FDA . . . Food and Drug Administration, Dept. H.E.W.

Plate 35

1. *Safety goggle: Typical of those used today by cyclists and sheriffs; made of base metal like brass or nickle silver; temples were totally covered with a material called "spaghetti" --a durable sweat-proof combination of woven cloth with thin plastic coating (like "oilcloth" used for table covers.) First worn about 1895 while driving the "horseless carriage" in the U.S. The model shown is dated circa 1920 and a product of the Willson Company, a manufacturer of safety goggles and still in existance. Most goggles were glazed with safety lenses. (See text.)*

2. *Safety goggle: With side shields; all steel; railroad engineer's type, but used for other protective purposes; circa 1900.*

3. *Safety goggle: All metal; same as #1, with comfort cable temples; circa 1915; made by American Optical Co., catalogue #3388 cc flat, of 1912 issue. Could be folded at the bridge and inserted into small case. Bridge was adjustable as to height and inclination. Called shooting or automobile goggle. Also made in 1/10 12KT gold filled. Lenses, clear or "smoked"(gray).*

Chemically Tempered

Ophthalmic Lenses

continuation

cluded that the original statement of policy concerning IRL, required alterations. Hence, revisions were made relative to IRL (35 FR 15402). The writer will deal with these modifications later in this article.

Protective lenses have been prescribed evidencing greater interest in regard to actinic, photic, and other non-mechanical malevolence, than in regard to potential physical trauma to the eye and adnexa. The Louvre in Paris exhibits one of the earliest examples of "safety" lenses as part of an armor circa 15th century. It was not until 1840 when protective lenses for workers began to make their appearance. Eye protective devices were used from wired-glass to mica in 1868, to lenses of gelatin, isinglass, and marineglas at the end of the 19th century. Safety lenses were pressed from clear and gray celluloid until as late as 1916.

Mr. Walter G. King, son of Julius King, the latter was founder of the Julius King Optical Company of Cleveland, can be considered the one person who supplied the greatest impetus to the development of safety goggles during the early 20th century. What with the horse-carriage and the industrial revolution, the need was precipitated. In 1912 Mr. King devised a crude air-heat tempering process following the techniques initiated to strengthen glass lamp chimneys. Mr. King's concern with eye injuries stemmed from the large volume of eye prosthesis fitted in industrial areas. In 1923 the company merged with American Optical. Mr. King was retained as the Safety Director. Since then, progress in their Safety Division has been legendary.

In 1930 Laminated glass was introduced as a result of an accident in a lab where a flask had been filled with a mixture of celluloid, acetone and alcohol and had been forgotten for many years. The contents during this time had evaporated to a thin dried residue adherent to the inner surface. A later mishap resulting from glass splinters caused Edouard Benedictus to return to this curious flask. Thus was formed the first sheet of "Triplex" laminated safety sheet glass.

From these beginnings evolved our present thermally tempered glass, laminated "Motex" and followed by thermosetting plastics circa 1950. The writer played an interesting role in the perfection of the latter.

The subject matter at present of utmost consequence which affect IRL at the doctor's level concerns the quality of the lens surface obtained after it has been processed by the conventional heat-tempered methodology then tendered acceptance by the profession and thereafter dispensed to the patient.

The writer must digress at this point to emphasize the obtuse chauvinistic ineptness of bureaucracy. In this instance the FDA, with respect to what occurs

to a lens of crown glass when it is subjected to heat treatment by the prevailing and accepted process. Precisely, all the advantages of precision surface grinding and polishing are dissipated; let alone, the incident of breakage, warpage, internal stress, mild discoloration, and an increase in the minimum thickness requirement obviated by the conventional treatment. Notwithstanding these basic single vision dilemmas, the fused type bifocal (Kryptok, flat-top, curved-top, Nokrome, etc.) presents additional problems brought about by the interference with the original annealing of the blank when the segment portion is fused in the forming of the rough bifocal blank.

The FDA does not specify a minimum thickness requirement for either glass or plastic lenses. The manufacturer of plastic lenses needs only to indicate in some manner that the lenses supplied meet the "steel ball test."

In 1965 a patent was granted to a Mr. Webber of the Brockway Glass Works which, in essence, provides a process of chemically tempering glass employing an exchange of ions initiated by an electrolytic solution. The same year a Dr. Kissler of the University of Utah received a patent for a direct method of chemically tempering of glass. For a number of years this latter method found application in the toughening of industrial glassware such as is used in laboratories and the automotive industry or usages where durability and longevity in glass are indispensable. Its application to lenses served no great purpose in the United States. Glass lenses were not required to be tempered. The handful where tempering was indicated could be resolved easily by employing the conventional air-heat tempering process.

However, England, Japan and many other countries have had the IRL requirement for a decade or thereabout. Consequently these foreign countries expressed a prior interest in this chemical process. Japan in particular developed an apparatus which could treat batches of lenses in quantities of approximately 25 of 500 and 1800 per cycle of 20 hours ±2 hours. (See illustration)

The chemistry which provides an end product in which the resultant lens is easily twice as tough as the prior air-heat tempering method involves an ion exchange in the surface of the glass. These chemically strengthened lenses offer a substantial and consistant advantage which include: 1) FDA requirements can be met and surpassed with much thinner lenses. (1.0 mm. have been tested in the writer's lab with excellent results). 2) Lightness of weight factor comparable to plastics. 3) Warpage virtually eliminated. 4) Highest in scratch resistance. 5) Minimum internal stress. 6) Notched rimless can be strengthened equally. (drilled lenses require some experimentation) 7) No change in water-clear color of lenses.

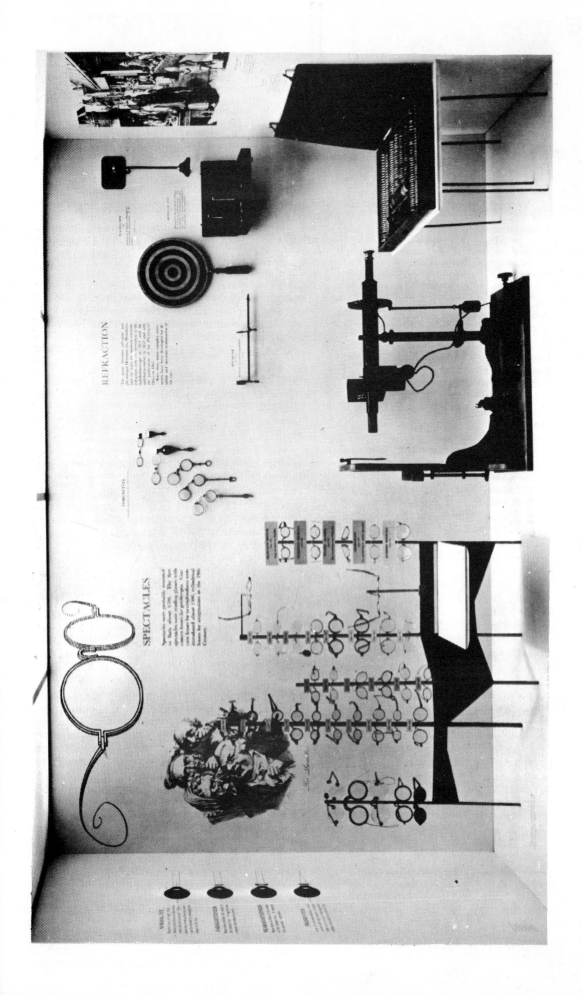

A DISPLAY COVERING VARIOUS OPHTHALMIC ENTITIES. ON THE LEFT WALL FOUR EYE CONDITIONS. CENTER WALL SHOWS LORGNETTES. RIGHT CENTER WALL IS A SHOWING OF A DISC WITH CONCENTRIC CIRCLES. THIS WAS USED TO MEASURE ASTIGMATISM. ON THE FLOOR TO THE LEFT A DISPLAY OF SPECTACLES. TO THE RIGHT OF THIS IS AN OPHTHAL-MOMETER* FOLLOWED BY A TRIAL SET*. ALL CIRCA FROM 17th TO LATE 19th CENTURY.

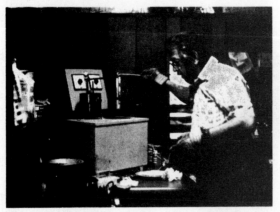

The tempering apparatus in the writer's laboratory contains two circular chambers each thermostatically controlled. One chamber to pre-heat the lenses, the other contains the chemical bath. Both chambers can hold chemicals, and can be used for phototropic lenses and the white and pink category. Each requirement is slightly dissimilar. A separate inexpensive small air-oven should then be used. Ths method serves to double the capacity. Current: 110 Volts, Single Phase.

Small preheating oven thermostatically controlled. Interior visable.

Photos by John Campbell

8) Reduced labor costs. (Cycle can be performed overnight, continuous attendance unnecessary) 9) Thinness of glass affords greater cosmetic appeal. 10) Breakage or fire-cracks totally absent, and finally, 11) No distortion due to creep* as experienced in plastic lenses.

Plastic lenses are supplied and produced using CR-39 as the monomer. Each respective source of supply manufacture these lenses employing a variety of curing cycles, chemical additives, accelerators, catalysts, and inhibitors. The final polymer varies in hardness (scratch resistant) thickness, base curve, color and most important, when lenses from different sources are dyed, the results are disastrous. (Elaboration of this, is a story of itself)

The patient transition from glass to plastics present many problems of spatial disparity and distortion of lens parameter. These conditions result from the newly created variations in the base curve of the plastic lens supplied. The writer is aware of improvements in the offing in the area of the scratch resistant quality of plastic lenses. Indeed, this would implement the future acceptance of these lenses.

The reader who is familiar with chemistry will grasp the basics of the transfer of ions, which takes place in the process, and how this strengthens the lens up to three times the toughness of the air-tempered method. The mechanics of performing the operation is so simplified that casual labor can be employed satisfactorily. Essentially, the chemical strengthening process involves the immersion of a batch of lenses in a salt bath at a temperature substantially below that of the melting point of glass and considerably below that employed in the alternate method. The glass lenses contain sodium ions while the salt bath contains potassium ions. The requirements for chemical equilibrium are reached and the ion exchange occurs between the bath and the surface of the crown glass. (Phototropic or flint glass require some slight variation in chemistry) (see schema) Precisely, the large potassium ions will diffuse into the glass surface to replace the sodium ions. This exchange produces so high a

surface compression as to surpass greatly the FDA requirements by at least three times that of what can be achieved by air-heat tempering. This method may offer an added advantage in the form of eliminating the need for testing each lens individually. A sampling from each batch can be "ball tested," providing proof that the balance was subjected to the same strengthening process. Testing of plastic lenses is performed in a similar batch sampling arrangement. This would also expedite record-keeping which is a FDA demand.

The writer is cognizant of a situation that has resulted involving the Corning Glass Works, manufacturer of Photogray™, Photosun™ and a host of conventional glass lens blanks among their many other glass products. This producer has been confronted with a serious potential reduction in their glass lens business. And what may be hurting even more is that this business has been moving towards the plastic lens manufacturers. Plastic lenses are considered equal to IRL. The present preponderance of the characteristics of plastic lenses which serve to a considerable advantage over the 2.2 thickness required of the glass lens is distinctly a worry to Corning. Especially when the monomer used to produce these plastic lenses, namely CR-39, is a product of Columbia-Southern Chemical Corp., a wholly owned subsidiary of Pittsburgh Plate Glass (PPG). Enough said!! Corning is now experimenting with a formulation of glass directed expressly for the chemically tempering bath method.

Apparatus for the purpose of chemically tempering lenses, as has been stated, is being manufactured in Japan and being imported into this country since the latter part of 1971. However, these models have been found to present a variety of problems necessitating revisions by American ingenuity. Information obtained by the writer has it that two companies, one in the East and one based locally in California are adapting these Japanese models so that they would perform satisfactorily. Corning is presumed to be working with two such improved models both of 500 lens capacity. One was apparently completely refurbished in Princeton, N.J., the other locally in Pico Rivera.

Rumor has it also that the impact resistant quality of the lens produced by the chemical process has only a two to three year wearing life, which for the intent is sufficient. However, it is difficult for anyone knowledgeable in chemistry to comprehend

*Creep . . . During process of polymerization, the plastic flow is uneven causing a wavy internal stress. This may occur also in the gel stage.

90

Actual display of change of styling from 1900 to (modern times) 1940; courtesy American Optical Company.

CHEMICAL PROCESS TABLE

Lens Processing	White Crown & Fixed Tint	Photochromic
Time	16 Hours	16 Hours
Temperature Of Salt Bath	420-450C (788-842F)	370-400C (698-752F)
Composition	99% Reagent grade potassium nitrate with addition of ½% silicic acid* and ½% sodium nitrate.	60% Reagent grade potassium nitrate 40% sodium nitrate

*Manganese may be substituted.   Schematic courtesy W. P. Keith Co.

a depletion of the potassium ion as a result of ordinary wear. This rumor may be purely hearsay and probably initiated by blatant competition.

"Thoughts are seeds of future deeds." This bit of philosophy is quite timely as we embark upon a new and historical adventure. What else but IRL? and its impending punishment.

One last bit of speculation—What is to become of the out-of-town O.U.—5.00 with the broken lenses emergency syndrome? This is still a function of the single lens air-heat tempering apparatus which affords almost instantaneous command, i.e. after the correct cycle is calculated for the lens in point.

It should also be noted that all prospective users of the aforementioned chemically tempering lens apparatus must enroll with the Research Corporation of America, of 405 Lexington Avenue, N.Y., N.Y. 10017. An initial tribute is invited in the form of a payment of $100.00 plus a royalty of twenty-five cents per lens dispensed to the patient. This royalty is based on the quantity tempered as in sun lenses where the fee could be as little as fractions of a penny. The Research Corporation of America is a non-profit organization devoted to sponsoring further development in all fields. All monies and grants are turned over to research endeavors. A truly worth-while organization.

The FDA does not require that the birefringence pattern be the criteria in testing for IRL. This pattern as we know is not seen in plastic lenses and the same situation is present with chemically tempered lenses. The only identifying mark must be applied prior to tempering. A small dot or line at the hidden bevel or under the strap of a rimless of any silver solution or paint prior to preheating the blanks will do the trick.

As with the conventional heat tempering the lenses must be edged and bevelled ready for mounting prior to the chemical bath. A secondary refinement of bevel or any operation which would interfere with the compression application could create a fracture of the surface. Further experimentation may resolve this provoking and often costly situation.

The application of this methodology to the strengthening of lenses is completely revolutionary and as such is thought-projecting for the inquisitive mind. The apparatus lends itself to an entire new field of exploration. The reader should also understand that the tempering process must be performed prior to the application of an anti-reflective or color coating. The writer has tried tempering coated lens and found to his dismay (or is it to his advantage?) that a coated lens will revert to its water-clear condition after being subjected to the chemical process. He is confident that the accomplishments offered by this newer process will be sizable before its maturation.

The questionable ruling of the FDA mentioned at the beginning of this article is concerned with the statement in the regulations "........................... all lenses must be impact resistant **except where the physician or optometrist finds that such lenses will not fulfill the visual requirements of a particular patient and direct in writing, etc., etc."**

What, precisely does this mean? The writer phoned the local FDA. Response to this question elicited an evasive answer. Something about strong lenses being thin in the center, these would not lend themselves to heat tempering, and that making this form of lens thicker in the center would negate its cosmetic appeal. Hog . . . wash. The basic intent of the regulation is defeated by such exclusions. The reader should avail himself of the penalties incumbent upon violators of rulings of the FDA. These amount to a fine of $1000.00 or one year in prison for each violation.

The ophthalmic dispenser (optometrist, ophthalmologist and dispenser where applicable) should know that the FDA ruling provides for optional IRL one lens replacement whenever the other lens or the glasses were purchased prior to the instance of the ruling. The FDA suggests also that an attempt should be made to induce the patient to have both lenses tempered. This applies also when a replacement of a frame is made.

A definite No . . . No! is the reply to the patient who cannot appreciate the efficacy of the safety factor requirement for his .150 stock zylo rimmed half-eye glass +1.00's which he uses only occasionally when reading at home.

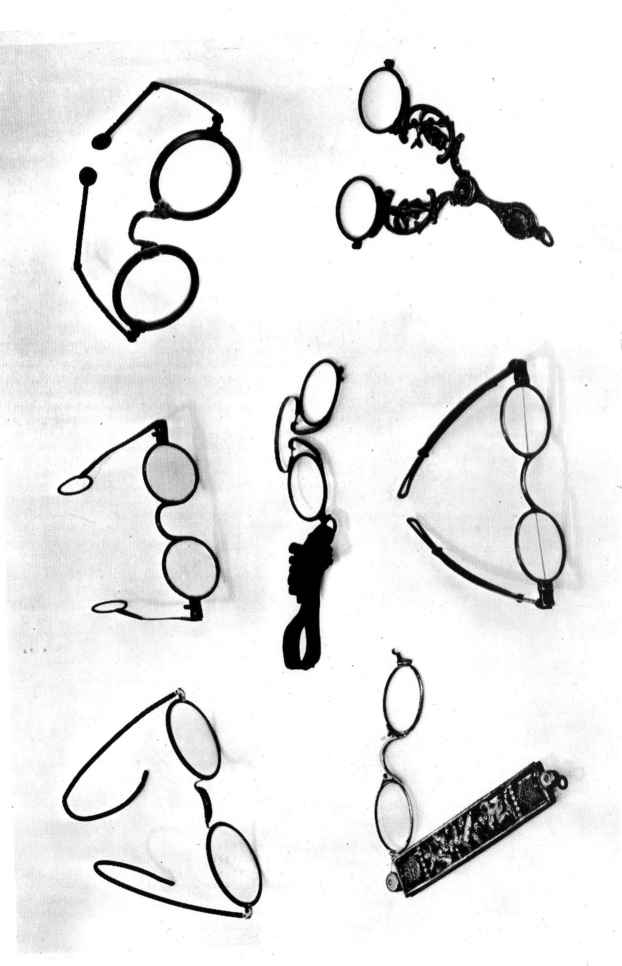

Collector's display of note showing top, left to right: Innerim C. 1930, spectacle C. early 18th century, Chinese C. 14th century. Middle: A.C. hard rubber eye glass steel spring and ribbon attached. Bottom row: Highly decorated lorgnette smaller size Chinese C. 19th century. Authentic spectacle with split bifocal C. Ben Franklin. Prototype lorgnette (scissors type).

A NEW PLASTIC LENS

Ed. Note — This article was written by our Associate Editor almost thirty years ago. It has as much merit today as when written. The Optometric World is publishing this as an example of our new policy of offering articles of great interest to Optometry. Dr. L. D. Bronson tried to market this development for two years without success. A friend of his, Dr. H. Feinberg, then assistant to the late Hudson Titmus, Jr. brought the development to Mr. Titmus' attention who apparently appreciated its potential. Titmus bought the process which is now "The Optilite Lens". Dr. Bronson not only provided a process of molding plastic lenses, but also a method of surface grinding rough and semi-finished blanks. The latter methodology is considered of greatest impact in today's market. Dr. Bronson's full length book, "Early American Specs", for the general public, is being published and will hit the book stores early in 1973.

The crusade to protect the eyes of our young and those engaged in eye-hazardous activities has had small impetus. It presents a conflict as timely and important as our present day all-out campaign to combat and destroy the ravaging forces of cancer, heart disease, muscular distrophy, polio, mental disease and a multitude of others. Here stands the challenge to all those associated with healing fraternities. This program should be supported, in their daily endeavors, by such motivating groups as optometrists, ophthalmologists, oculists, ophthalmic dispensers, public health workers, and societies for the sponsorship of better sight and the prevention of blindness.

Have we ever paused to consider that when the ophthalmic practitioner writes a prescription for eyeglasses, he may be unleashing a potential implement of destruction of the human eye? The very same glass lens which traditionally has caused an unconscious fear of physical injury to the eyes of the wearer, can reverse its primary objective and play the villainous role of eye-maimer.

How often are members of healing fraternities confronted with any number of familiar and gruesome incidents related by their patients? The following case depicts one instance amongst many to be found in the annals of ophthalmic literature, to wit: The young lad was running while playing. He tripped and fell. He was wearing shatter-proof spectacle lenses. The terrific impact received by these lenses when they hit the hard concrete pavement caused a substantial fragmentation of the glass. A razorsharp sliver pierced the upper lid at the fold, severing the two superior extra ocular muscles. The surgeon was summoned. He performed the familiar emergency restoration and repair type of plastic surgery. Both parent and patient suffered needless mental and physical distress.

The writer's personal experiences in both research and in private practice, with respect to the recent successes in the field of hard resin lenses, has induced him to maintain the greatest confidence in the future popularity of hard resin lenses as an imposing measure of eye protection for the young, the industrial worker, and other groups of eyeglass wearers. The new hard resin plastic lens offers immeasurable advantages, in addition to the accepted therapeutic purpose of spectacle lenses.

More than 10 years ago the writer was engaged in war work — particularly concerned with lenses for gas masks. It was known that the wearing of the gas mask presented certain problems. The soldier who wore corrective lenses discovered that these lenses would fog when the mask was in place. This condition obviously lowered his visual efficiency. The men invariably sought relief by discarding the gas mask. In actual chemical warfare this maneuver would have proven disastrous. The writer's interest was aroused. An attempt was made to correct the existing difficulty with anti-fogging lotions. This method proved unsatisfactory. Further investigation revealed that transparent plastic, such as methylmethacrylate (acrylic group) responds more readily to temperature changes than glass, thus minimizing condensation and as a result diminishing fogging. All plastic possesses the favorable characteristic of low thermal conductivity. An attempt was made to surface grind a thermoplastic (lucite) to a focus. Assiduous successive trials resulted only in a quality of surface unfit for spectacle lens use. This prototype plastic lens developmental work was very discouraging. This took place over 10 years ago, (Ed. Note — Now almost 30 years). In California (1937-1939) the Tulca Lens was introduced to the profession. The poor scratch resistant ability of this lens together with numerous other unsatisfactory characteristics resulted in its ultimate rejection.

In this constantly changing world we may be

inclined to pause and contemplate the rapidity with which transformations occur. Tremendous advances have been made in all phases of scientific pursuit. We now have atomic radiation being directed to peaceful pursuits in industry and medicine. In dentistry we note the influence of the florides and the improved methods of drilling. Since then, in the ophthalmic field considerable advancement has been made in plastics, for contact lenses, spectacle lenses, simulated crystaline lenses and plastics for corneal transplants.

In ophthalmic literature very little will be found regarding plastic in its relationship to spectacle lenses. The practitioner may be interested in some brief comments on certain differences in types of plastic.

In the sizeable province of the chemistry of resins, organic plastics are found to be classified in two major groups. These are known as thermoplastic and thermosetting plastics. A truly thermoplastic material softens when subjected to temperature increases until it reaches such a state of pliability that it can be stretched and molded into complex shapes without any appreciable change in its chemical structure. When cooled, a thermoplastic hardens and shrinks. This hardening and softening cycle may be repeated indefinitely without decomposition or deterioration of the plastic material. In this group is found the acrylics, plexiglas, lucite) cellulose acetate, cellulose nitrate (zylonite), polystyrene, vinyl, etc.

The second group are the thermosetting plastics which first soften when heated, then harden. This transformation into a solid is called polymerization. The relationship between the time and temperature required in the hardening process is known as the curing cycle. If the temperature is increased sufficiently (above 300° F) the material decomposes without melting and without substantial softening. Members of this group are known as the allyl resins, the melamines, phenolics, polyesters, ureas, etc.

The thermoplastics lend themselves readily to severe forming operations with the application of pressure and temperature elevation. Thermosetting plastics, on the other hand, are preferred for purposes where dimensional stability and heat resistance are imperative.

Within the past few years great strides have been made in the field of transparent plastics, particularly in the thermosetting polymer group. These newer organic esters of low volatility lend themselves readily to low temperature compression-impression castings, and their properties are most desirable for ophthalmic lenses. These precision castings offer the following characteristics, which are self-descriptive: 1) Impact resistant and superior tensile strength. In effect, shatter-proof and unbreakable. 2) Less affected than glass by welder's spatter and high velocity particles thrown-off by grinding wheels.

3) Dimensionally stable unaffected by relatively low or high levels of temperature, will not shrink, expand or soften in relatively high temperatures. 4) A minimum of 40% less weight and 5% more transparent than glass. 5) Fewer concentric rings of reflection are visable in high minus lenses. 6) Impervious to ordinary household chemicals, including acetone, benzene, paint remover and carbon tetra chloride. 7) Possesses greater abrasion and scratch resistance than any other known plastic. 8) Fogging of lenses reduced by 60% to 75% as compared to glass. 9) The lens will retain its clear water-white color indefinetely. 10) Finally, the molecular structure of the basic material is such as to make it more versatile than glass in the application to the range of foci, types and tints. With ordinary use and care these new lenses will remain as clear as glass, even after the usual change of prescription is indicated. They will outlast the usual interval between prescriptions.

The original developmental work on this material in relationship to its application to ophthalmic lenses was first begun by the writer over three years ago. Eight months of this time was spent in research work at the Dade County Medical Research Foundation Dr. L. R. Newhouser, Capt. Ret., U.S.N.M.C., the director of the Foundation was very enthusiastic concerning this project. His experiences in naval hospitals provided the momentum for this enthusiasm. The writer is grateful for his good fortune in being afforded the opportunity to further the development of his work on plastic lenses. His association with eminent research fellows added considerable ramifications to the proposed extent of this work. A good deal of thought was directed to the possible application of this plastic material as a post-operative prothesis in cataract removal. More serious work can be projected towards a program concerned with the preparation of a series of transparent simulated crystalline lenses to occupy the cavity remaining after the removal of the cataractous lens. The subject of plastic corneal transplants requires further and intensive investigation. Plastics have served to replace wasted human bone structure and disfunctioning heart valves.

As a result of this research and developmental work, the writer has devised a method of compression-molding which, to his knowledge, is unparalleled in the field of thermosetting plastics. This unique process is employed in the design and production of "Medilens", the new plastic lens. The production of these lenses and the research work on the projects mentioned above will be continued at the Opto-Medical Research Laboratories where facilities are made available to the willing research worker. The writer wishes to extend an invitation to members of the profession to visit the laboratories and observe or engage in the work of the future.

Fine collection courtesy American Optical
Co. First specimen improperly dated could
be Revolutionary Circa. Fourth and seventh
specimens excellent examples of early sunglasses C. 18th and C. 19th century respectively.

96

"THE EYEGLASS VENDOR," PAINTED IN 1864, DRAMATIZES THE PROGRESS OF
OPHTHALMIC PROFESSIONS IN THE SERVICE AND CORRECTION OF HUMAN VISION.

Eye Glasses of Old

For 600 years, style and science have marched hand in hand to produce better vision for better living

1260—Glasses with immense crystal lenses set in frames of carved ivory were worn by Chinese aristocrats

1550—In the days of Good Queen Bess, glasses were widely worn. They had large round lenses with horn rims

Eyeglasses of the 1500's. The frame is of bone and pivots on a rivet. They clamped on the nose.

Eyeglasses typical of the 1500's—of horn, with bridge constructed to give it "spring."

German eyeglasses of about 1650. Some had holes in the rims, through which cord was strung and looped over the ears.

In the early 1700's, spectacles were invented with metal sides ending in large loops that clamped against the temples. These are of iron, with inner rims of horn.

George Washington wore these spectacles. They have hinged sides ending in loops. A ribbon could be run through the loops to tie the spectacles on.

Chinese spectacles. Tortoise shell rims with cord ear-pieces and movable carved nose-piece; used in China 250 years ago.

Old Chinese spectacles. Rims of horn; sides hinged, with solid round ends for clamping against the head.

1780—Benjamin Franklin, inventor of bifocals. He halved and combined his distance and his reading lenses

This "wish-bone" lorgnette has elaborate arms of silver and is of a style popular in France under the Directoire.

A tiny spy-glass forms the pivot of this fan.

An ivory lorgnette of pre-Revolutionary France. It was in reality a "spy-glass," used for distance seeing.

A "quizzer," or "monocle for the hand," popular in the middle 1800's. This one embodies its owner's watch key.

1830—Spectacles were used for indoor tasks; but in public, a lady invariably carried a small lorgnette

Tortoise shell and gold lorgnette with a hinged bridge. About 1850.

Spectacles of 1800, with sliding ear-pieces adjustable in length.

Folding gold lorgnette with pivot bridge. About 1848.

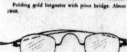

Spectacles of 1860, with hair-thin frame of blue steel wire.

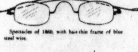

Folding oxfords of 1875, with rims of thin shell and bridge of flat blue steel.

Another style of oxfords of 1875, with flat blue steel nose spring and lenses rimmed with hair-thin blue steel.

The first of the "modern" spectacles. Thin wire frames of blue steel; sides that curve behind the ears.

Quaint old eyeglasses with fan-shaped, cork-faced nose guards and reinforced nose-bridge.

Old French eyeglasses, pince-nez, rimmed with silver; cork nose guards and intricate spring bridge.

Two little prongs to fit on the eyepits helped hold these old eyeglasses at the proper angle.

Old French pince-nez eyeglasses with cork guards and high-arched silver bridge.

Old French rimless spectacles, with tiny lenses; ribbon bridge and ear-pieces of silver.

An oxford of about 1900, finely wrought in solid gold with gadroon engraved rims.

1900—Pince-nez glasses were quite the thing. These daring young sportswomen wear theirs on a ribbon

The earliest recorded concave (myopic) spectacles. Painting by Jan van Eyck.

BENJAMIN FRANKLIN, BY HIS INVENTION OF THE BIFOCAL LENS IN 1784, GAVE THE
GREAT GIFT OF YOUTHFUL VISION TO GENERATIONS OF SPECTACLE WEARERS.

THE FRESNEL* MATERIALIZATION

There are happenings in history which at the time were considered of little or no consequence with respect to their impact on civilization, particularly in the arena of the healing professions. The now classical advent of Nobel Laureate (1945) Sir Alexander Fleming's* incident with penicillin (1928) (his brother figured prominently in the ophthalmic fraternity) (Alexander Fleming also discovered lysozyme) and consider the monumental discoveries of Louis Pasteur*, Koch* and Lister* as but a modicum of attestation in point. Let us not overlook the incident of the accidental discovery of laminated glass by the chemist Eduard Benedictus (1930) which led to shatter-proof safety lenses and Kevin Tuohy's failure to check his lathe when making an adjustment to the edge of a rigid contact lens resulting in the smaller more effective overall diameter . . . . as the legend goes. History is embellished with many such vignettes and mankind profits by such discoveries and they are called *progress.*

One such a man was Augustin Jean Fresnel (1788-1827), a French physicist noted for experiments on aberration and diffraction of light. In an effort to provide funds needed to continue his experimentation, it became necessary that he seek outside employment. He obtained the post of engineer for his government. While so employed he took upon himself the task of improving the intensity of the beam of light produced by its source as emitted by the local coastal lighthouse. He found that the optical system providing the warning beam was inefficient and thus less effective. He devised a method of focusing and concentrating the incident reflected ray employing a thin sheet of glass which contained a series of concentric simple lens sections or zones each constructed so as to retain all the optical qualities of a lens of the diameter of the glass. See diagram plate #1.

The same principle had a later application in the automotive industry in which the focusing apparatus is constructed in a like manner using molded plastics in lieu of glass. This seemingly unpresumptious change has not only resulted in simplification of its manufacturing process but has reduced the cost of this item to a minimum.

The present utilization of the Fresnel principle has reached out in innumerable tangents in the area of ophthalmic lens application. In England a low cost temporary Fresnel spectacle has been designed (see photograph plate II) by Edward Marcus, LTD. as a "give-away" in powers of +12.00 and +14.00 diopters. The healing process following an operation for the removal of cataracts often takes months before a proper prescription can be dispensed. The usual procedure has been to allot the patient plano sunglasses as a protection/from glare and a tem-

porary hand magnifier as an aid for reading. Some of the more fortunate or more affluent could obtain the loan of a fairly useful pair of biconvex cataract spectacles which had to be returned to the hospital at the time permanent glasses were dispensed.

In England the greatest percentage of this type of surgery is performed under the prevailing health scheme . . . . National Health Service (NHS) or the Department of Health and Social Security (DHSS). These plans resemble our Medi-Cal and Medi-Care however remote the similarity may be. In England, any person requiring health-care can obtain this service without cost, be he native, alien or on a temporary visa.

The Marcus Aphakia-Spec (trade name) can be purchased from the vendor at 0.60 Pound Sterling per completed pair. (In U.S. currency $1.55) or in lots of 100 at 0.50 Pound Sterling. Other specifications are as indicated: The lenses are injection moulded probably from an acetate compound to a rigid thin flat lens. The mold marks and a some-

(Photos: By John Campbell)

Good Resolution with Japanese Fresnel Magnifier Thickness 0.50 mm.

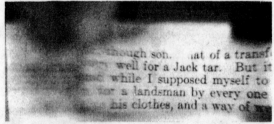

Eyes magnified greatly while wearing Marcus Fresnels of plus 14.00 D.S. Not Unlike Conventional Lens. Advantage of weight and thickness most important factors.

what hazy sector is visible in the upper central quadrant. Information has it that special tools are being designed to improve the quality of this Fresnel. The lenses are 1.6 mm thick and are tinted *mouse* color (very light brown). The frame is also of the injection moulded class about .175 stock, with a 22 mm bridge and is of 46mm eye, statesman shape. The color of the frame simulates demiamber; the lenses are set at a pupillary distance of 62 mm. The total weight of frame and lenses is 20 grams or approximately ¾ ounce.

Fresnel lenses unfortunately offer some reduction in maximum visual acuity obtainable . . . . . , a loss of about half-way between 20/20 and 20/25 or one-half Snellen line. Similarly, it is unfortunate that the NHS cannot provide for a better quality of temporary optics. However, this low cost Fresnel

*Fresnel (Pronounced Frenell) . . . Engineer-Physicist
*Sir Alexander Fleming . . . Bacteriologist
*Louis Pasteur . . . Bacteriologist
*Robert Koch . . . M.D.
*Sir Joseph Lister . . . M.D.

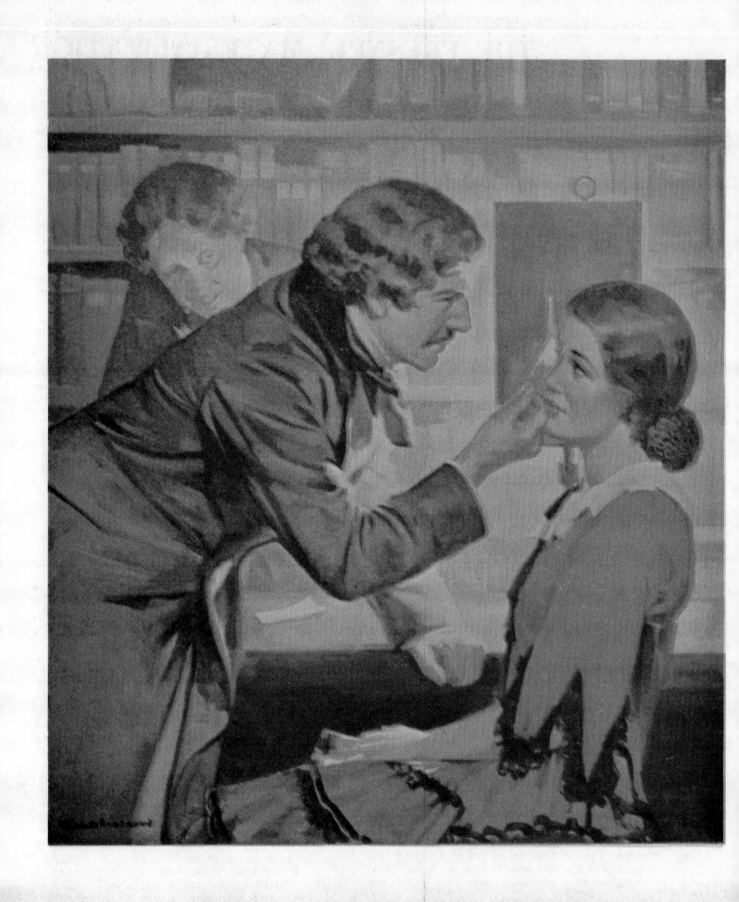

HERMANN VON HELMHOLTZ, WITH HIS OPHTHALMOSCOPE (INVENTED 1851), SAW THE
INTERIOR OF A LIVING EYE AND FOUNDED THE SCIENCE OF PRECISE EYE EXAMINATION.

Making
Metal Frames
Pan Out

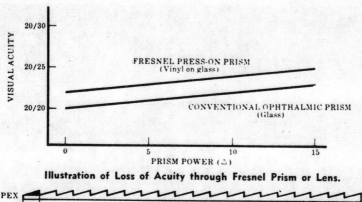

Illustration of Loss of Acuity through Fresnel Prism or Lens.

Actual measurement with thickness gauge of 1.6 mm.

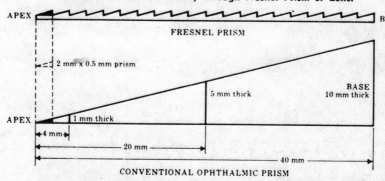

Fresnel Prism Contains all the properties of the Conventional Prism.

Typical Press-On lens segment to meet special gaze requirements.

Example of small, out-of-the-way segment for unique needs.

Intermediate segment over bifocal before deciding on optimum multifocal lens.

Special applications of Press-On Elements

application serves as important post-operative cataract purpose.

Japan for a number of years has been producing and exporting a "pop-out" give-away type of Fresnel magnifier (see plate #3) with a focal length of about two inches, designed so that it can slip in and out of its plastic case not unlike a lorgnette. The case simulates pinseal leather and can be imprinted. Its application is directed especially towards retail entrepreneurs who can use this as an advertising medium.

This Japanese imported counterpart of the Fresnel admittedly served as the prototype for Derek Marcus in his early attempts to apply the thin lens principle to reduce the thickness and weight of the conventional cataract lens system. (September 1970, British Optical Press Correspondence columns) Experiments with this Japanese version were also being conducted in a hospital in Northern England. The final visual resolution was the most severe problem encountered. It was finally decided that as a temporary spectacle the somewhat diminished visual acuity is negligible in relationship to the purpose

it serves which is, as termed, of a temporary or emergency nature. In this country these advertising *gimmicks* can be purchased in quantities with the imprint for fifty cents each. It should be mentioned here, that the Japanese magnifier model of the Fresnel lens has much finer optics than the one supplied by Marcus. It appears to be a compression moulding from transparent sheet stock not more than 0.50 mm in thickness.

In this country application of the Fresnel principle has taken on an aura of tremendous proportions. Optical Sciences Group, Inc. of San Rafael, California is involved in three major functions: 1. The manufacture of Press-on Optics (described later). 2. The production of highly sophisticated tools for the compression molding of the Fresnel type of lenses, mirrors and prisms which serve to a great advantage not only for ophthalmic usage but in the field of photography, the film industry and for many other optical application, some as yet undiscovered. 3. Continuous research in the entire field of vision-care. The group is composed of optometrists, ophthalmologists, bio-physicists, elec-

IN EUROPE, FROM THE 14TH TO 17TH CENTURIES, STREET VENDORS SOLD CRUDE
SPECTACLES, BOTH FOR ADORNMENT AND AS AN AID TO VISION.

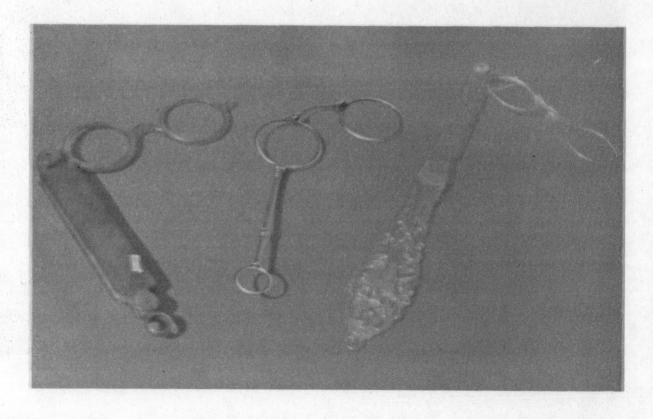

tronic specialists and others. The work includes the development of automated devices for health screening in which the human eye is employed as the means of detection. (See Optometric World, July, 1972 issue *Optical Fair '72 To Remember*).

Press-on optics, the trade name for this most ingenious application of the Fresnel principle is formed by compression moulding of a transparent polyvinyl chloride (PVC) flexible in character. It is classified as a thermoplastic material which softens when subjected to temperature increases. This characteristic is of no great detriment unless the lens should be inadvertently left on the dash-board of a car and should remain exposed to the direct sunlight for a long stretch. This could completely destroy its optical properties and its effectiveness. However, it will not deform under the usual ranges of temperature.

The writer initiated a series of experiments with Press-on optics early in May when he was assigned to do a column both on this commodity and *Photochromatism*, (sort of a consumer's research bit). The following will comprise the writer's findings and personal experiences with wearing his own prescription prepared with Press-on optics and the results obtained with other forms of the series of Press-on optics. It should be understood by the reader that the only *visual panacea* exists solely in the realm where anyone is blessed with O.U. 20/20 from birth 'til death (A little gleam of Time between two eternities—Carlyle). Members of vision-care professions are fully aware of the paucity of such rare encounters.

The writer's interest was provoked when he experienced an incident in his practice where the prescription requirement called for the incorporation of prisms O.U. of eight diopters; an amount just sufficient to induce single binocular vision and ensure a proper depth perception. The recipient patient was a mere fourteen years of age, female and pretty, who vowed to continue *sans specs* and remain in her so called state of euphoria, unless she could have "groovy glasses". "I once had those *bottle bottoms* when I was *young*. I will never wear them again. I caused them to become broken." Two prior attempts at corrective surgery, which resulted in utter failure, had precipitated the parent's rampant determination to abandon any further attempts at surgical interference. The writer pledged a cosmetic interpretation of "groovy eyeglasses." The final prescription was designed to interpret the prism formulated with the Fresnel Press-on elements. The carrying lenses, planos, were provided in base curve of 6.50 D. This latter specification is presumed to preclude reflections, and to act as a deterrent to any potential peripheral aberrant, and for the most effective adherence of the secondary element. The lenses were shaped in the rimless "in style". Well! you should have seen the gleam in the eye of the patient when the glasses were dispensed. Words from this humble writer would be but a small impression of her expression. A feeling of excited exhuberance seemed to permeate the scene. Her very action exemplified a sense of prevailing adoration.

The readers may question the practicability, effectiveness and even to the shelf-life of so comparatively a new application of the Fresnel principle. In his laboratory, the writer has attempted to accelerate any possible abuse to these lens elements and simulate an extended time-cycle of wearing period by subjection to numerous potential and commonly occasioned degradations. These experiments were conducted in the writer's small but efficient laboratory (consumer advocate testing). As a result, and considering his personal wearing of the lenses and what he learned from some of his human "guinea pigs", he can safely advise, with reservations, however, that this present application of Fresnel optics is to be considered an additional bold tool to be "reckoned with" in the armamentum of the vision-care community, however, it's somewhat wanting of perfection.

The young female mentioned above was unaware of the vertical parallel indentations which are co-incident and slightly visible to the observer. This condition is an integral effect of the Fresnel pattern of construction just as is the concentric circles in the spherical lens application. The expected slight loss in visual acuity was apparently subjugated to the advantage of improved binocular perception and the overall feeling of elated satisfaction.

Other questions which may crop up could be concerned with the extent of time this form of Fresnel lens will remain adherent to the carrying lens. For the case in point, the advice given to the parent indicated the need for reaffirmation of the effectiveness of the prescription within six months. Definitive and explicit instructions on the continuous care were both oral and written and handed to the parent and patient.

Research scientists at the Optical Science Group (Press-on Optics) have indicated that with ordinary care in accordance with instructions, they have found their product will remain intact for the usual extent of time between eye examinations. A representative from the Group stated that with proper care Press-on optics will remain adherent for an indefinite period of time. A verbal interview with the Group forewarned the writer that laboratories affixing these elements must exert extreme caution when working with these overall or segmental elements especially to be concerned with the following recommendations: 1. Press-on units should never overlap the perimeter of the carrying lens. It should always be cut smaller than the main lens by at least 0.5 mm. This applies to the area around the straps of a rimless mounting. The obvious purpose for this device is to forestall the possibility of *touch* which could cause detachment of the Fresnel element from the carrying lens. 2. The present instructions which are included with the product indicates that running tap water be used when applying the units. This should

be deleted and in its stead replaced by a small pan of mineral-free water (purchased in food markets). Both carrying lens and the Press-on should be wetted thoroughly not just moistened and in the submerged position apply one to the other, then "press-out" the residual air. It has been found that much of the tap water contains an abundance of inhibiting minerals. 3. Prior to attachment the elements must be thoroughly cleansed employing as a solvent vehicle any of the stock contact lens refined detergents as Titan, Clens and LC 65. It is also important to make certain that no residue remains on the respective surfaces and that a lint-free cloth be used for drying purposes. Our laboratory has found that the flexible Polyvinyl chloride of which the Press-on units were made, will absorb water and turn a yellowish color if a more caustic detergent is used during the cleaning process. Whenever the units are inadvertently allowed to remain submerged in water for any extended period, they will form a hazy residue on the surface. This is an indication that water has been absorbed. In the event the water was not demineralized, problems will be encountered when attempting to cause it to revert to its original mirror-like quality . . . and the optics may be spoiled. If purified water is employed and absorption occurs just by permitting the elements to remain between thin absorbent material or soft cloth, the invasion of the water will be dissipated. 4. If the elements are made adherent to plastic lenses which have been dyed extreme caution should precede their application to make doubly certain all the coloring media is completely removed. Perhaps, contact lens detergent used in processing the elements will suffice, otherwise minute particles of the coloring material will be absorbed by the Press-on unit and be retained. This may present some alternate problem later on.

Press-on optics are currently being produced by the Optical Science Group in a multitude of lens forms specifically oriented towards areas in the ophthalmic field where they will serve to the greatest advantage. These follow and are accompanied by the writer's comments for each: 1.) As an alternate to conventional prisms and/or lenses for the purpose of reduction in thickness and weight and of course, enhancement of cosmetics. 2.) As a substitute for forms of lenses in short supply; those impractical to manufacture, such as, prism bifocal segments, double segments, special add combinations, uncommon or eccentric placement of segments of unlimited size or shape, slab-off prism segments, segments for oversized lenses requiring abnormal decentration, segments for phototropic lenses (bifocals have been in short supply), and many more not listed here. If any of these forms of lenses are available from the usual sources, their cost is not only exorbitant but delivery date is often uncertain and may create hard feelings or even cancellation from the patient. 3.) Excessively high powered segments with corresponding compensating prisms

for low vision correction. 4.) Prism base in or out for near point use only in single vision lenses. 5.) Phototropic lens trifocals (unobtainable). 6.) Temporary trial prototype bifocals, prisms or whole lens.

Optical Science Group has indicated that they have available a low visual acuity kit of D25 segments of precalculated prism controlled in adds of +3.00, +4.00, +5.00, +6.00, +7.00 and +8.00. Base in prism is incorporated in each addition and as much as 17 prism diopters total is available in the +8.00 diopter add.

The trial kit can readily serve to ascertain an immediate response from the low vision acuity patient. The trial kit contains all the above adds in left and right trial rings. Once the proper add is determined the Press-on adds can be immediately affixed to the ocular surface of the distant prescription.

It should be remembered that all new products must undergo a lengthy consumer's appraisal (both patient and doctor . . . a lesson we should have learned from the FDA's apparent failure with the flexible lens). Many discouraging problems may ensue before an approach to perfection will be attained. Nevertheless, Press-on optics is so obvious an aide, the writer feels he is not remiss in suggesting that his readers try a sampling for their own edification.

There appears to be no end to the ramifications to be spun-off as satellites when one pauses and reflects on the potential application of the Fresnel principle, to wit: Its possible use in aniseikonia, antimetropia, underwater masks, motorbike goggles, lenses for the correction of the operators acuity when using cameras, microscopes or any fixed focal length eyepiece. The writer can also ponder the potential problems which may present themselves as a result of improper handling by the "not so careful wearer." In this area we may find: Impatience resulting from the continuous separation of the elements: The hazard resulting from the slight reduction of acuity in patients where maximum vision is critical. The presence of waviness and/or aberration resulting from the combination of elements, and the patient's complaint that the new lens magnifies or diminishes the eye size not unlike the conventional lenses.

Let science march on!

113

Plate 36

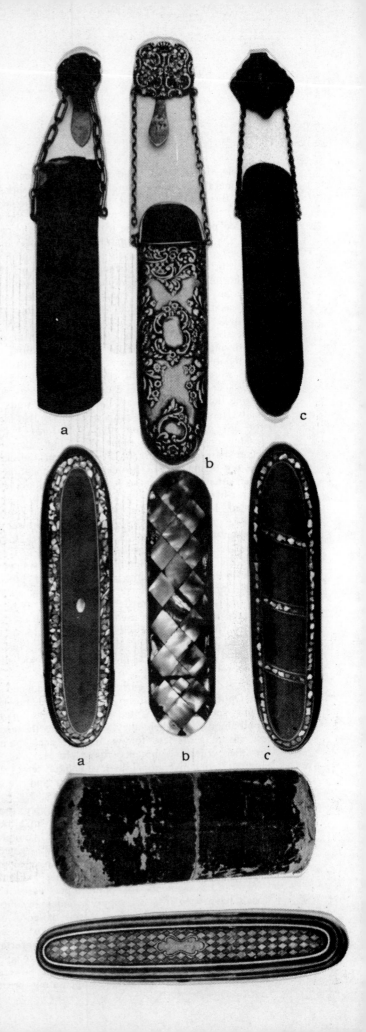

1. *Spectacle case: a) Paper mache body covered with leather; chain nickel plated over brass; medallion, openwork black enamel over same metal; circa 1880; original wholesale selling price $7.50 per dozen; can bring $25.00 each easily at antique shows. b) All sterling silver with silk plush (velvet) inner portion which would come in contact with spectacles; marked sterling; very rare; in excellent condition; circa 1880; present value $100.-00. c) Pinseal leather over paper mache; chain steel; medallion, leather with central bronze insignia symbolizing music, being a bird perched on sheet music; clef clearly defined; circa 1870.*

2. *Spectacle case: a & c) Long and narrow 1 1/2" x 6 1/2" constructed of paper mache, covered with a hard substance like celluloid and inlaid with mother-of-pearl chips; resembles Chinese beetle-ware but black; opens from top, obviously to hold the thin narrow frames of circa 19th century; brings $15.00 at antique shows. b) Mother-of-pearl entire body; part of collection of Martin Evers (see photo) who claims it to be circe 1780; rare.*

3. *Spectacle case: Paper mache; opens virtually in half; inscribed Aug. Nichols N.Y., dispensing optician late 19th century; case measures 2 1/4" x 5 1/2" to hold larger lens size spectacle.*

4. *Spectacle case: Silver; lined with silk plush; stamped Pat'd Jan. 24 1860; measures 1 1/4" x 6 1/4"; this type was made in 3 different sizes in "extra heavy planished* tin" and sold for $10.00 to $13.00 per gross wholesale; circa 1880.*

114 **Planish: Metal pounded thin.*

Assortment of cases showing different approaches to their utilization; circa 19th century.

115

Plate 37

1. *Spectacle case: German nickle-silver; measures 1 1/4" x 4 1/4"; circa 1880.*

2. *a) Eyeglass case; pinseal leather throughout; shaped to afford least stress of eyeglass; measures 1 3/4" x 4 1/4"; circa 1880. b) Silver monocle or quizzer case; lined in plush; hand-engraved C.H. Mount 424 W. 23rd St. New York; circa 1860. c) All steel; heavy duty; circa Pre-Civil War.*

3. *Spectacle case: a) Open Morroco case; 6 1/2" long, 1 3/4" wide; gold leaf stamping; A.S. Marshall Optician jeweler; Rutland Vt.; circa 1800; specimen in excellent condition. b) Extra long paper mache; 1 1/2" x 7" to accommodate straight temples; circa 1870. c) Paper mache covered with thin leather; inscribed J.P. King, Scientific Optician, Springfield, Mo. (See text under CHEMICALLY TEMPERED LENSES.)*

4. *Eyeglass case: Steel body covered with thin leather; allowance for pad projection from eyeglass center made in body of case; snap button closing; circa 1870.*

5. *Eyeglass case: Later model than #4; slightly larger; circa 1890.*

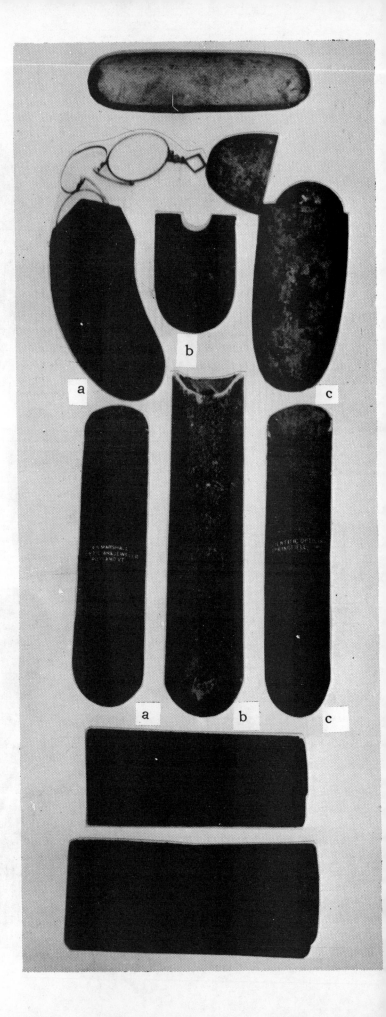

Plate 38

1. *Spectacle case: a) Leather covered paper mache; extra long; circa 1890. b) All leather with special catch; circa 1890. c) Leather covered paper mache; opens at top; circa 1890.*

2. *Spectacle case: a) Cowhide; heavy body moulded rough stitched; circa 1870. b) Leather over paper mache; inscribed M.L. Stein, Oculist-Optician, Detruit, Mich. c) Open end; resembles real horn or Chinese beetleware; gold leaf imprinted J.M. Cood, Optical parlors, Louisville, Ky.; circa 1860.*

3. *Spectacle case: a) Short eyeglass case; leather over paper mache; open end. b) Large A.O. goggle case; inscribed E.B. Megrovitz, Fifth Ave. New York; best quality leather; interior plush; circa 1910. c) Small open end leather over paper mache; inscribed A.P. Hall, Optical specialists, Visalia Calif.; for eyeglasses; circa 1900; measures 1 3/4" x 4 3/4".*

EYE POLLUTION

Optometric World, July, 1973

What thoughts would traverse the minds of our most profound thinkers in the realm of all disciplines of eye-care? Were they to learn that the wearing of ordinary eyeglasses could be a direct cause of cancer, at the maximum, or in the least, effect a substantial alteration of the human endocrine system?

At one point in the early history of eyeglasses, it was thought that the wearing of glasses was attributed to the work of the devil. As late as 1583, Dr. George Bartisch, the famous German ophthalmologist, severely condemned their use and indicated this in the abundant renderings issuing from his quill.

Recently, an article appeared in the leading national weekly in which a reknown dermatologist makes a definitive statement as follows, "I have encountered a number of cases of facial skin cancer in which the patient was a person who had worn rimless spectacles for years." He contends, furthermore, "At certain angles, the lower edge of the eyeglass acts as a magnifying glass — concentrating sunlight into small bright areas of the skin at the tumor site. Apparently these rays are not strong enough to produce a detectable heat. But, they do create a concentration of ultra-violet rays which are known to damage the skin."

This writer felt sufficiently motivated to reply and offer an updated version of the wearing of rimless spectacles. This involves the recent F.D.A. regulation regarding impact resistant lenses limiting rimless glasses to plastic lenses, which absorb ultraviolet rays. Consideration also must be given to a proper adjustment of the spectacles so that they will not impinge a predisposed situs. The same modality applies to any spectacle. Here, topical contact at the derma presents a vulnerable site.

The relative impact made by ultra-violet rays upon the specific susceptable area needs further amplification. This study falls in the domain of the work of Dr. John N. Ott, whose talents are exposed at the Environmental Health and Light Research Institute in Sarasota, Florida. Dr. Ott states that we need to know much more about natural and artificial light and what it does to us and to the plants and animals sharing our world. Modern technology has made obsolete our old ideas about light.

"How do most of us live?", he asks. "We wear glasses. We look through the windshields of our cars. We watch T.V. We work under artificial lights, often in windowless buildings or buildings where the windows can't be opened. *We wear tinted sunglasses* and attend nighttime sports."

All these aspects of everyday American life are the direct results of our sudden technological advances. Most of us take light for granted, without stopping to ponder the possible effects of substituting neon. fluorescent, strobe, black light, or *tinted eyeglasses* for natural sunlight.

In his recent book, publication date of May 1, 1973, Dr. Ott presents startling studies and case histories which show the subtle effects this new technology is having upon our physical and mental well-being and the development of our children. The book, published by The Devin-Adair Company of Greenwich, Connecticut, contains 208 pages of well-documented material which should serve as a stimulus to the thinking optometrist to venture still further into seemingly foreign scientific specialties in an effort to advance their objectivity — their approach to alternate aspects of the visual apparatus.

Dr. Ott's book is replete with multitudinous presentations indicative of the role played by light, particularly in the range of the ultra-violet wave length. "*Health and Light:* the effects of natural and artificial light on man and other living things."

In his laboratory, Dr. Ott has shown conclusively that various kinds of lighting conditions could affect the physical condition of live animals. Not only did alterations to the light source cause external changes, but also to *sex life* and the *life span.*

The key to all this, to quote the doctor, seems to lie in the simple act of the light pathway entering the human eye. Changes were noted when sunglasses were worn, in distinction to a period without sunglasses. When the subject was exposed to *full spectrum* lighting or natural sunlight without the encumbrance of any sunglasses, the physical conditions became improved. And, depriving the man of ultraviolet can become a strong obstacle to the improvement of one's health. Nevertheless, we manage to survive.

Corning Glass, Imperial Optical of Canada, Armorlite, American Optical Corporation, House of Vision, and Obrig Laboratories, at some time did produce *full spectrum lenses* both in glass and plastics. This writer made additional inquiries and found, to his chagrin that all these companies discontinued the manufacture of such glass excepting for those produced in plastics by Lunarlite of Glendale, California and Obrig Laboratories of Sarasota, Florida, where *full spectrum* contact lenses can also be obtained. A *full spectrum symbol* appears on all eyeglass lenses, especially developed for this specific purpose.

Dr. Ott makes continued use of his expertise with his time-lapse camera. He employs this methodology to research secrets of cellular reaction to light over a continuous and prolonged span of time. In this manner, he can assess the long-time activity of a plant or animal in a short period of time.

Grants to the Foundation he supervises will support research at the Stretch Medical School at Loyola University of Chicago by Anthony Marchese, an associate of Dr. John Ott. This is the fifth year of a project aimed at identifying the photo receptor mechanism of the retina and how it functions in stimulating the pituitary and pineal glands by means of the neuro-chemical channels. A number of recognized scientists have now determined that part of the eye has a *non-visual function of influencing the endocrine system.*

"This was a wild idea — really far-out," recalled Ott, "that light entering the eyes influences the endocrine system which controls basic body chemistry through production and release of hormones."

In other studies Dr. Ott has shown the existence of a positive relationship between light, environment, and *tumor development* in both mice and men.

The Environmental Health and Light Research Institute associated with New College should receive accolades from our profession. A complete revelation germaine to the wearing of eyeglasses may result from the continued research at the Institute. Optometry should support such efforts. In the least, every optometrist should read carefully the book written by Dr. Ott. The Devin-Adair Company will mail it upon receipt of $7.50.

The WESTERN OPTICAL WORLD

| VOLUME IV | | NUMBER X |

April 1918

Gordon Grant

Will YOU supply EYES for the NAVY?

9

ABOUT SUNGLASSES

The origin of protective glasses to serve as a barrier against the discomforting and harmful reflections of the sun's rays stems from the primitive use of minute perforations and slits in opaque protective material which in some simple fashion was held before the eyes. This method of escape gradually gave way to spectacles glazed with absorbtive colored lenses. Colored glass did not come into being until the latter part of the 16th century. The earliest reference was to green glass manufactured in England in 1561. Pierson of London, in 1672, sold blue glass. In 1767, George Adams, also of London, advertised smoked glass and called it "grey." Sunglasses were found to exist in the latter part of the 16th century. In the Seventeenth Century Venice was the source of most of the colored glass. At the time, Venetian glass was revered wherever it was used.

The Eskimo constructed sun goggles from wood and walrus skin. These wrapped around the face and temples and were tied behind the back of the head. The front vision area consisted of a narrow horizontal slit which permitted the passage of only a small percentage of the sun's incident rays.

In ancient Tibet fine horsehair was woven in such a manner that it acted as a sun visor when placed in front of the eyes.

The first American record of sunglasses came from an advertisement of James Peters of Philadelphia, who announced the sale of white, green, blue and gray lenses. In 1885, William Thompson of Philadelphia produced amethyst tinted glass from windows tinted by long exposure to the sun's rays.

Almost all glass was imported from Europe prior to 1867. Following that time, America successfully produced its own glass which was so far superior that the Europeans turned the tables and imported glass from America. Many attempts were made to produce glass in America prior to 1867, but most ended in failure both for the lack of quality of the product and financial reasons. From 1872 on, a variety of colored lenses were perfected, each supposedly possessing more unusual properties for absorbing harmful light rays. It is perhaps more correct to praise the advantages of all tinted lenses for their faculty of absorbing some of the incident light.

Plates *#39* & *40* show a number of examples of both American and European specimens of sunglasses. In addition to the ray interference quality of colored glass,

Plate 39

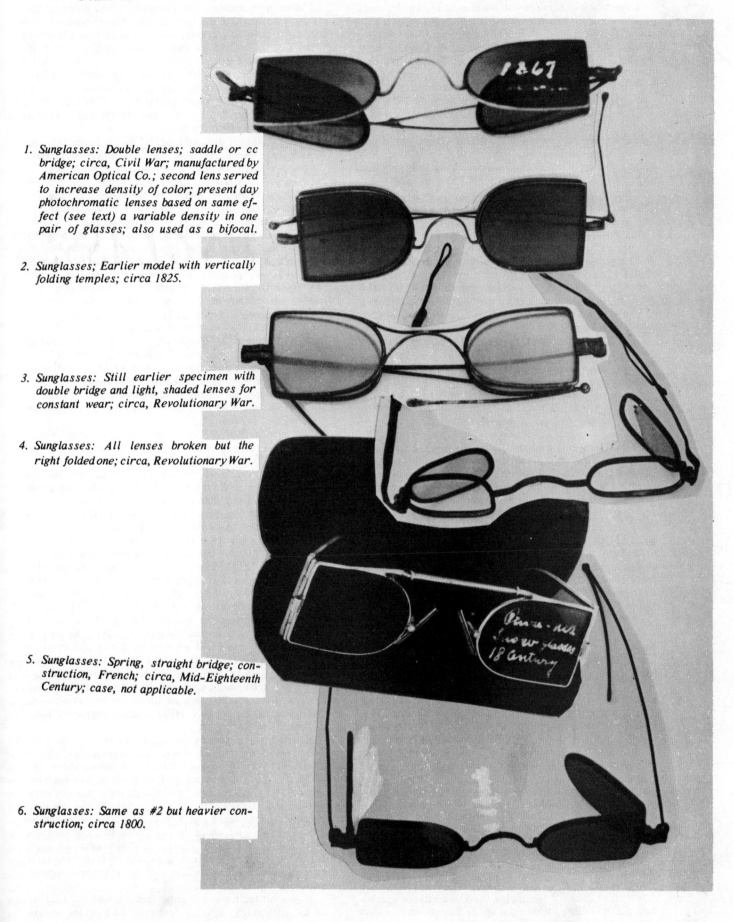

1. Sunglasses: Double lenses; saddle or cc bridge; circa, Civil War; manufactured by American Optical Co.; second lens served to increase density of color; present day photochromatic lenses based on same effect (see text) a variable density in one pair of glasses; also used as a bifocal.

2. Sunglasses; Earlier model with vertically folding temples; circa 1825.

3. Sunglasses: Still earlier specimen with double bridge and light, shaded lenses for constant wear; circa, Revolutionary War.

4. Sunglasses: All lenses broken but the right folded one; circa, Revolutionary War.

5. Sunglasses: Spring, straight bridge; construction, French; circa, Mid-Eighteenth Century; case, not applicable.

6. Sunglasses: Same as #2 but heavier construction; circa 1800.

a philosophy seems to have developed throughout the ages which is still prevalent. Investigators claim there is a relationship between color and emotion. The tremors resulting from Parkinsonism have been reported to diminish materially when one so afflicted wears green lenses, thereby eliminating the red rays which presumably have some exciting influence. Claims have also been made that certain tints have a therapeutic or restorative property. These claims, however, are unsubstantiated at the present time. Red is supposed to act as a stimulant; with green, on the other hand, having a calming effect. It should follow then that the wearing of lenses within the borders of the green wave length should act as a tranquilizer, since the response should be diametrically opposite to that when wearing lenses in the red category; but these suppositions are all conditional and should be interpreted with caution.

About 1969 a variable transmission lens was developed, the basic formula for which was produced by Corning Glass Works of Corning, New York. The blanks are ground and polished by Corning licensees to form all prescriptions including bifocals and plano (non-focal) lenses. These are called by the Corning trade name of "Photogray." The lens possesses a unique characteristic of changing shades in accordance with the intensity of illumination to which they are subjected. When worn in the bright sunlight they turn dark, which is accomplished by the phototropic additive incorporated when the batch of molten glass is prepared. The lens gradually returns to approximate water clearity when worn in a less luminous atmosphere.

Phototropic adaptations have been studied as far back as 1881. An article written by John H. Carter, O.D., Ph.D., for the Journal of the American Optometric Association, presents documentary evidence of this. The article also states that the American Optical Company is still researching the potentialities of phototropic lenses produced of impact resistant plastic. If ever developed, this would virtually displace its present glass counterpart. The glass is heavy and must be subjected to a special heat treatment to instill the safety factor now an FDA requirement. The heat tends to impart a slight yellowish cast which some wearers find objectionable.

Corning is now providing blanks which will produce a darker shade when the lens if fully exposed. The author feels this will find greater acceptance. The fully-exposed first photogray lenses still are not sufficiently absorbent for exceedingly bright sunlight.

Sunglasses, or "shades," the pseudonym frequently applied by the Southern gentry, particularly those of darker skin tones, have always been part and parcel of the offerings of the entire ophthalmic field from manufacturer to vendor or dispenser as an ancillary ware. Some form of sunglass has been known to exist ever since the historically undocumented event of Emperor Nero, to whom the author has alluded previously. The function of sunglasses has always been to serve as an appliance of therapy, protection and--often--dramatics. 1) Therapy, for psychosis and neurosis or simply to hide discoloration (Eccymyosis*) and/or disfiguration of eyes, and adnexa*; 2) protection against the harmful glare factor its primary function and 3) dramatics, obviously to add a touch of mystery. Within the last decade this latter application has been accentuated especially by the "rock groups." Colored lenses in such "groovy" shades as blues, yellows, browns, reds and some tones of green, grey and rose are part of the accoutrement of being "in" or "aware." Some apparently approach sending the wearer on a "trip*."

In "Head Shops," spectacles can be purchased glazed with purple colored lenses not unlike bicycle or highway reflectors with multiple facets which cause a sequence of visual hallucinatory apparitions when viewing a light source, particularly a black or stroboscopic light.

Modern technology has produced other glare protection devices within the past decade. Tinted plastic lenses in any shade or intensity and a coated lens are among the devices which, at the present writing, offer the greatest advantages. The effective principle of the latter is produced by partially silvering one surface, usually the inner surface, making the lens a transparent mirror which reflects away about 25% of the incident glare rays. It is similar to that which is used by the Fuzz* in their one-way observation room.

Another scientific method is the polarized lenses which have been available for several decades. However, they have not proven too successful or popular for a number of reasons, uppermost being that the true polarizing compound must be laminated between two pieces of thin glass and then ground and polished to lens prescription or "plano." This often makes the cost prohibitive and furthermore, the lens is thicker than normal and tends to be weighty and, additionally, the lamination has been known to separate. Polarized lenses do, however, possess a distinct advantage where reflections from surfaces interfere with visibility in deep water. All maritime activities involving the highly reflective water can be classified in the area where polarized lenses are of optimal advantage.

Near the end of World War I, the "war to end all wars" with the inception of aero-warfare, the need for flying goggles brought about designs which are still functional and are being imitated and reproduced by present manufacturers to fill the void created by the scarcity of the originals at this time and the substantial demand for this type of eyewear.

Throughout World War II, the "war to end all wars" the flyer's goggles was of general issue (G.I.) for all members of the Air Corps. There are some such goggles still in existence. At the beginning of the war the accepted 1/10th 12K yellow and white gold-filled grade of metal was used. However, civilian use was prohibited in an effort to conserve the precious metal in the gold-filled frames. This metal, of critically short supply, could then be diverted to the war industry where it was of more strategic use at the moment. Apparently the civilian population aspired to relate to and condone wartime activities as an expression of patriotism by wearing and exhibiting the goggles as a badge of acceptance in the same manner as a political button. This feeling sparked a tremendous demand for the G. I. aviation goggles. The Korean and Vietnam crisis, "the wars of attrition," also created inroads on the optical industry to provide aviation goggles. The feeling of the community this time, with respect to their relations to the war, appears not to be one of approval. Nevertheless, the author finds difficulty understanding why these new groups are again looking to the G. I. issue aviation goggle for their personal eyewear.

In addition to glasses for the usual therapeutic purpose, i.e. correction of visual abnormalities and oculo-muscular imbalance and related symptoms, there are snow glasses, sun glasses, pinhole glasses, slit glasses, auto glasses, phototropic glasses and glasses for perceiving mountains of euphoric dissertations when viewing stroboscopic or black lights (glasses glazed with faceted lenses of a violet shade but of fluorescent complexion, mentioned previously). There are also sunglasses worn for the sole purpose of serving as a cover-up for the tell-tale signs of the drug abuser; the contracted or distended pupil and "blood-shot" eyes.

A general feeling can thus be deduced that the wearing of all spectacles serves a dual role: as a protective faculty and as a social or political badge.

Plate 40

1. *Sunglasses: Patented frame; real tortoise shell. See #6, this plate, for special construction showing separation of front sector of plastic shaded crescent shape lens from rear sector which is clear and without any lens. Acted not unlike a sunvisor and similar to present graduated lens. Top portion dark and bottom portion clear; for day and night purposes.*

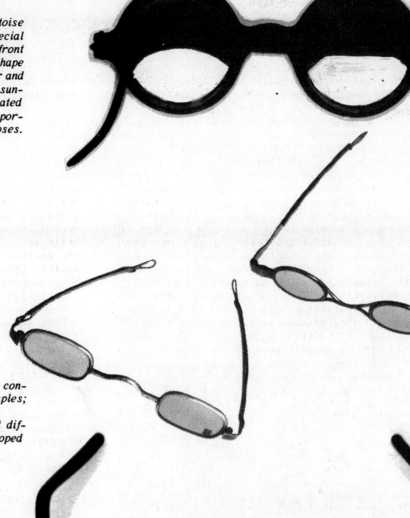

2. *Sunglasses: Earliest model bronze construction; heavy duty; adjustable temples; circa, Pre-Revolutionary. (See text).*

3. *Sunglasses: Same circa as #2 but difference in ridge construction and in looped temple.*

4. *Sunglasses: Celluloid rims; metal comfort cable temples; coquille amber lenses; circa Pre-World War I.*

5. *Sunglasses: Keyhole type bridge; split joint temple; lenses cracked but of blown smoked glass (coquille); frame black acetate; mass produced type of sunglass; circa, Post-World War II.*

The origin of protective glasses to serve as a barrier against the discomforting and harmful reflections of the sun's rays stems from the primitive use of minute perforations and slits in opaque protective material which in some simple fashion was held before the eyes. This method of escape gradually gave way to spectacles glazed with absorbtive colored lenses. Colored glass did not come into being until the latter part of the 16th century. The earliest reference was to *green glass* manufactured in England in 1561. Pierson of London, in 1672, sold *blue glass*. In 1767, George Adams, also of London, advertised smoked glass and called it **grey**. Sunglasses were found to exist in the latter part of the 16th century. In the Seventeenth Century Venice was the source of most of the colored glass. At the time, Venetian glass was revered wherever it was used.

The Eskimo constructed sun goggles from wood (see illustration) and walrus skin. These wrapped around the face and temples and were tied behind the back of the head. The front vision area consisted of a narrow horizontal slit which permitted the passage of only a small percentage of the sun's incident rays.

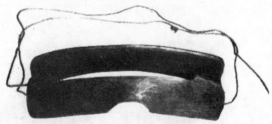

Sun-Visor, Eskimo, hand made carved from wood, ca. early 19th century. Courtesy: Smithsonian Institution.

In ancient Tibet fine horsehair was woven in such a manner that it acted as a sun visor when placed in front of the eyes.

The first American record of sunglasses came from an advertisement of James Peters of Philadelphia, who announced the sale of white, green, blue and gray lenses. In 1885, William Thompson of Philadelphia produced amethyst tinted glass from windows tinted by long exposure to the sun's rays.

Almost all glass was imported from Europe prior to 1867. Following that time America successfully produced its own glass which was so far superior that the Europeans turned the tables and imported glass from America.

Many attempts were made to produce glass in America prior to 1867, but most ended in failure both for the poor quality of the product and finan-

cial reasons. From 1872 on, a variety of colored lenses were perfected, each supposedly possessing more unusual properties for absorbing harmful light rays. It is perhaps more correct to praise the advantages of all tinted lenses for their faculty of absorbing some of the incident light.

In addition to the ray interference of colored glass, a philosophy seems to have developed throughout the ages which is still prevalent. Investigators claim that there is a relationship between color and emotion. The tremors resulting from Parkinsonism have been reported to diminish materially when one afflicted wears *green lenses*, thereby eliminating the red rays which presumably have some exciting influence. Claims have also been made that certain tints have a therapeutic or restorative property. These claims, however, are unsubstantiated at the present time. Red is supposed to act as a *stimulant* with green, on the other hand, having a *calming effect*. It should follow then that the wearing of lenses within the borders of the green wave length should act as a tranquilizer, since the response should be diametrically opposite to that when wearing lenses in the red category; but these suppositions are all conditional and should be interpreted with caution.

A patented Sun-Visor circa 1920. The moon-shaped upper segment of flat celluloid construction tinted bluish green about 60% intensity outset nine mm. from the rim of the split-joint real tortoise shell frame. The lower segment is non-encumbered. (Author's collection)

About 1969 a variable transmission lens was developed, the basic formula for which was produced by Corning Glass Works of Corning, New York. The blanks are ground and polished by Corning licensees to form all prescriptions including bifocals and plano (non-focal) lenses. These are called by the Corning trade name of **Photogray.** The lens possesses a unique characteristic of changing shades in accordance with the intensity of illumination to which they are subjected. When worn in the bright sunlight they turn dark, which is accomplished by the phototropic additive incorporated when the batch of molten glass is prepared. The lens gradually returns to approximate water clearity when worn in a less luminous atmosphere.

Phototropic adaptations have been studied as far back as 1881. The first scientist to have observed

Plate 41

1. *Sunglass: Early type; circa, Revolutionary War.*

2. *Sunglass: Eyeglass hoopspring; blue steel; hard rubber eyerims; circa 1890.*

3. *Sunglass: Rimless with hoopspring and Kitcham and Mac Dougal reel; circa 1910.*

4. *Sunglass: Same as #3 but with thin silk cord looped through lens into which a hole had been drilled; circa 1889.*

5. *Sunglass: Slip-over; all plastic; produced and patented by L. Grossman of O.P.C.; circa 1920.*

6. *Sunglass: Called shooting glass; center clear; periphery ground glass; purpose of concentrating vision for better aim; circa 1870.*

what we now know to be **photochromatism** was ter Mer who demonstrated that a compound containing potassium salt exhibited a change of color when exposed to exciting radiation. (Ed. Note: Dr. Bronson's article **PHOTOCHROMATISM** appeared in the November '72 issue of the **OPTOMETRIC WORLD.**)

American Optical Company is still researching the potentialities of phototropic lenses produced of impact resistant plastic. If ever developed, this would virtually displace its present glass counterpart. The glass is heavy and must be subjected to a special heat treatment to instill the safety factor now an FDA requirement. The heat tends to impart a slight yellowish cast which some wearers find objectionable.

Corning is now providing blanks which will produce a darker shade when the lens is fully exposed—**Photosun.** The author feels this will find greater acceptance. The fully-exposed photograph lenses still are not sufficiently absorbent for exceedingly bright sunlight.

Sunglasses, or **shades,** the pseudonym frequently applied by the Southern gentry. particularly those of darker skin tones, have always been part and parcel of the offerings of the entire ophthalmic field from manufacturer to vendor or dispenser as an ancillary ware. Some form of sunglass has been known to exist ever since the historically undocumented event of Emperor Nero, to whom the author has alluded previously. The function of sunglasses has always been to serve as an appliance of therapy, protection and — often — dramatics. 1) Therapy, for psychosis and neurosis or simply to hide discoloration (Eccymosis) and/or disfiguration of eyes, and adnexa; 2) Protection against the harmful glare factor its primary function and 3) Dramatics, obviously to add a touch of mystery. Within the last decade this latter application has been accentuated especially by the *rock groups.* Colored lenses in such "groovy" shades as blues, yellows, browns, reds and some tones of green, grey and rose are part of the accoutrement of being in or aware. Some apparently approach sending the wearer on a *trip.*

In *Head Shops* spectacles can be purchased glazed with purple colored lenses not unlike bicycle or highway reflectors with multiple facets which cause a sequence of visual hallucinatory apparitions when viewing a light source, particularly a *black or stroboscopic light.*

Modern technology has produced other glare protection devices within the last decade. Tinted plastic lenses in any shade or intensity and a coated lens are

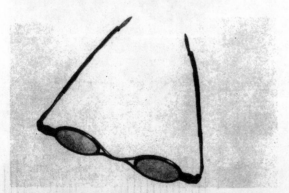

Spectacles glazed with tinted lenses. Chinese, bronze frame. Dated 800 A.D. Lenses of quartz. Courtesy Smithsonia Institution. (Author's note: The authenticity of this specimen has been challenged in the writer's book. In fact, many of the spectacles reposing at the Institution have been incorrectly marked. A reevaluation will ensue with the publication of the book "Early American Specs.")

among the devices which. at the present writing. offer the greatest advantages. The effective principle of the latter is produced by partially silvering one surface. usually the inner surface. making the lens a transparent mirror which reflects away about 25% of the incident glare rays. It is similar to that which is used by the *Fuzz* in their one-way observation room.

Another scientific method is the polarized lenses which has been available for several decades. However, they have not proven too successful or popular for *regular spectacles* for a number of reasons, uppermost being that the true polarizing compound must be laminated between two pieces of thin glass and then ground and polished to lens prescription or "plano." This often makes the cost prohibitive and furthermore. the lens is thicker than normal and tend to be weighty and, the lamination has been known to *separate.* Polarized lenses do, however, possess a distinct advantage where reflections from surfaces interfere with visibility in deep water. All maritime activities involving the highly reflective water can be classfied in the area where polarized lenses are of optimal advantage.

Near the end of World War I, the *war to end all wars* with the inception of aero-warfare. the need for flying goggles brought about designs which are still functional and are being imitated and reproduced by present manufacturers to fill the void created by the scarcity of the originals at this time and the substantial demand for this type of eyewear.

Throughout World War II, the *war to end all wars* the flyer's goggles was of general issue (G. I.) for all members of the Air Corps. There are some such goggles still in existence. At the beginning of the war the accepted 1/10th 12K yellow and white gold-filled grade of metal was used. However, in an effort to conserve the precious metal in the gold-filled frames. so that this metal of critically short supply could be diverted to the war industry where it was of more strategic moment. civilian use was prohibited. Apparently the civilian population aspired to *relate to and condone wartime activities as an expansion of patriotism by wearing and exhibiting the goggles as a badge of acceptance in the same manner as a political button.* This feeling sparked a tremendous demand for the G. I. aviation goggles. The Korean and Vietnam crises, *the wars of attrition,* also created inroads on the optical industry to provide aviation goggles. The feeling of the community this time. with respect to their relations to the war. appears *not to be one of approval.* Nevertheless, the author finds understanding difficult as to why these **new groups are again looking to the G. I. issue aviation goggle for their personal eyewear.**

In addition to glasses for the usual therapeutic purpose, i.e. correction of visual abnormalities and oculo-muscular imbalance and related symptoms. there are snow glasses, sun glasses. pinhole glasses, slit glasses, auto glasses, wind glasses, ski glasses. shooting glasses, motorbike glasses, phototropic glasses and glasses for perceiving mountains of euphoric dissertations when viewing stroboscropic or black lights (glasses glazed with faceted lenses of a violet shade but of fluorescent complexion, mentioned previously). There are also sunglasses worn for the sole purpose of serving as a cover-up for the telltale signs of the drug abuser; the contracted or distended pupil and *blood shot* eyes.

A general feeling can thus be deduced that the wearing of all spectacles serves a dual role: as a protective faculty and as a social or political badge.

Plate 42

1. *Sunglass: Earliest specimen of those mass produced by B & L; thin steel frame pressed endpieces; sold originally to retailer at $5.00 per dozen; circa 1900.*

2. *Sunglass: Rimless; saddle bridge; American Optical; circa 1920.*

3. *Sunglass: Innerim type; circa 1920.*

4. *Sunglass: Same as #2 but oval lenses.*

5. *Sunglass: Same as #1; circa 1897.*

6. *Sunglass: Same as #2; circa 1921.*

7. *Sunglass: Same as #2; circa 1921; English.*

PHOTOCHROMATISM*

The first scientist to have observed what we now know to be *photochromatism* was *ter* Mer who demonstrated that a compound containing potassium salt exhibited a change of color when exposed to exciting radiation. This introduction, to what has become an important study in chemistry, occurred in 1876.

In 1881 T. L. Philson noted that his neighbor's gateposts changed colors whenever bright sunlight was incident upon it. It was covered with a paint which contained *lithopone*. This reversible process was then called *actinic phenomenon* and served to describe this transformation in the diffuse reflection characteristic of the chemical *lithopone*. Later, in 1899 W. Marckwald coined the more descriptive term *phototropy* as representative of the process in which a solid substance changes color when exposed to the visible rays of light and reverts to its original color when returned to the dark.

Since this early observation other scientists have discovered that this phenomenon of *phototropy* is effective on other states of matter and that this transformation is not limited to the visible area of the spectrum. In more recent years **photochromatism** has become the term of popular choice as descriptive of the phenomenon.

The history of optometry is replete with milestones from which are hewn plateaus of considerable impact upon the effectivity of the visual apparatus. The pragmatic state can be said to have its beginning as recently as the mid-nineteenth century when Herman Ludwig Ferdinand Von Helmholtz discovered the Ophthalmoscope followed by his partnership in the breakthrough with the Keratometer; the De Zeng Skioptometer; McAllister's first cylindrical lens to correct the yet little known astigmatic error; the great work of Dr. Prentice and later Dr. Peckham; that of Gullstrand which won for him the Nobel Prize in physiology in 1911.

We must not omit identifying with the momentous efforts in the interest of progress performed by the optical industry and the ophthalmic laboratories. Improved methods of grinding and polishing glass lenses, precisely; diamond impregnated surface grinding laps and generating wheels; the change from simple red and white rouge to such polishing vehicles as cerium oxide, stannous oxide and the like; refinement of machinery and equipment to its present status of automated perfection.

The production of glass, in this scheme of things, experienced a history which from its very beginning was disappointing . . . *a dilemma*. Whenever attempts were made at a profitable venture from a usable material, the operators were met with what appeared to be inevitable failure. It required decades of persistance and perserverence before a quality of glass was produced which could provide the basis for a proper ophthalmic lens.

The essential raw chemicals involved in the making of glass are simple enough and similarly is the principle involved. Yet, some spontaneous and mysterious syndrome seemed to plague the efforts of the pioneers. The formula for the making of glass is 1. sand, 2. sodium, 3. limestone. Pulverize and mix well, heat and cool. This tremendous feat is effec-

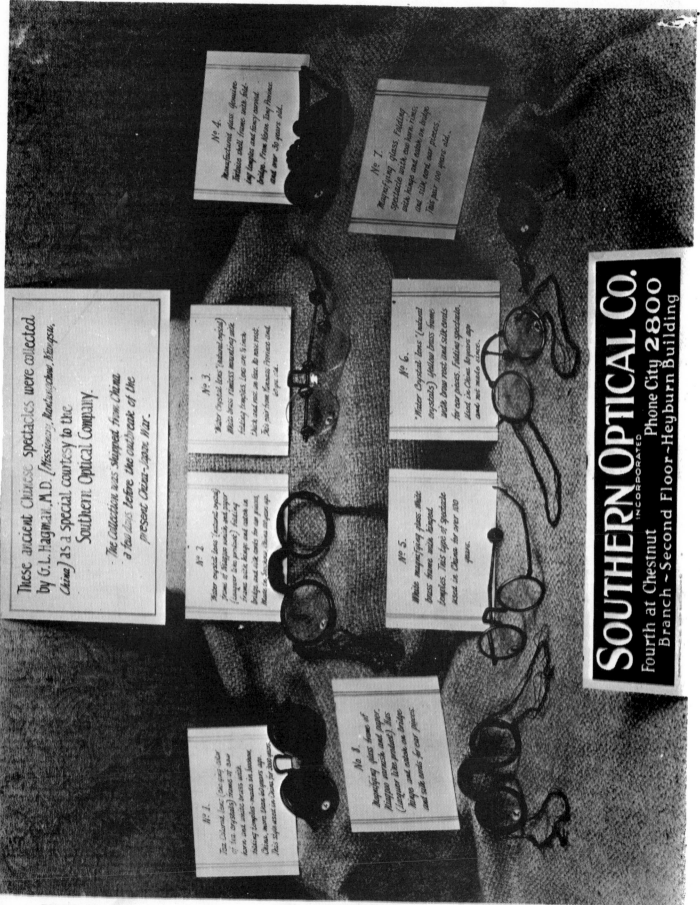

PLATE 43 a

G. L. Hagman M.D. Old photo courtesy American Optical Incorporation. 129

tively performed in modern times by Pittsburgh Plate Glass, Owens-Illinois Glass, Libby-Owens-Ford Glass, *Corning Glass Works* and Anchor Hocking Glass in order of rank with respect to size.

Photochromic glass consists of a variation of these very same ingredients to which is added crystallites in the form of silver halides. Exposure of photochromic glass to ultraviolet light results in photolysis of these suspended halide crystals. This photolysis produces electron-hole pairs that absorb visable light. During the bleaching process, electrons (or holes) diffuse toward the carrier of opposite charge. When the separation of oppositely charged carriers becomes less than some critical value, recombination occurs.

Many crystals exhibit a like characteristic. However the silver halides have been tested to offer properties most suitable for ophthalmic lenses. These very characteristics are presently being appropriated for use in architecture and the automotive industry amongst others.

A halide is a salt in which the anion (negative charged ion) is a halogen. Halogens (*hals* sea salt) represent a family of non-metalic elements which combined easily to produce salts. It is of the seventh group of the periodic table. Halogens are multivalent. This chemical process is not as complex as it may appear to the less informed. Those inclined to more extensive investigation should read the text "Photochromatism*" which elaborates in greater detail. The book consists of articles written by the most prominent research chemists engaged in this highly specialized field. The book is volume III of **Techniques in Chemistry."**

It should be interesting to note that the photochemical apparatus of the visual system resembles that of the chloroplasts in several general features in their absorption of light in the visible region. These processes are initiated by specific *photochemical* reactions which are followed by specific secondary *biochemical reactions.*

Rhodopsin is a lipoprotein which contains the chromophore *retinal.* Absorption of light by the complexed retinal initiates the visual process. The entire process is a photochromic reaction.

Photochromatism is present in many forms. It literally means a coloration by light: photo (light) and chrom (color) the suffix "ism" indicates a phenomenon. Photochromatic glass at present is being produced by Corning Glass Works of Corning, New York under the trademark of Photogray and Photosun. The latter refers to a darker series.

Specifically compounded basic minerals including the photochromic halide crystals are pulverized and heated to a temperature until they fuse into a molten state. These are automatically poured into metal molds of predetermined size, shape, thickness, and radius of curvature. Thereafter the molded glass is permitted to cool gradually which includes provisions for proper annealing. Annealing glass blanks insures deletion of strain factors and other impure qualities.

These molded blanks are shipped to *Corning licensed* processing plants where they are prepared in a finished and semifinished form. These blanks are then sold to the local laboratories for further processing. Much of the finished lenses are sold by some of the factories through their own outlets direct to the consumer who in this instance is the doctor or dispensing optician. Of course, not at the same price as to the laboratory operator.

The Corning molded blanks series has been de-veloped to provide plano lenses, finished single vision lenses 58 rd (Japanese) 62 mm (Shur-on/Continental) 62 mm (A.O. Masterpiece) 62 mm (Webster) and others, also finished bifocals, of the executive type and plus and minus one-piece A segment (both from the local laboratory, the latter is in very short supply). Note: *Shur-on/Continental was the first to supply finished single vision lenses.* All processors of Photogray™ and Photosun™ must be licensed by Corning and so indicate this on the lens envelope. It is presumed that other glass manufacturers are restrained from producing Photochromic glass because of *clandestined industrial courtesy. (You do your thing. I do my thing.)* Photogray™ and Photosun™ are only trade names. Photochromatism is a generic term and free to be used by all.

The advent of the appearance of Photogray™ followed by Photosun™ is surely a noteworthy advancement in the area of ophthalmic lenses and must be considered another milestone. The Corning Glass Works should be extended *fragrant bouquets* of the highest order.

At the level of the dispenser, be he optometrist, ophthalmologist or optician certain problems will be encountered. Advance precautionary measures should be taken as an aid to the proper understanding of the characteristics of the lens; *to wit:*

1. Thickness is a function of both the intensity of the shade and the speed of transformation.
2. Inherently, the thicker the lens the greater the probability of failure to return to clear white.
3. Anti-reflective coatings must be applied with great caution or else the photochromic transformation factor will be altered.
4. Number (3) applies to the tempering of lenses. Chemical tempering of lenses least destroys the effectiveness of the halides.
5. Finished lenses processed by different companies may act differently.
6. In cases of severe anisometropia or antimetropia a color difference may be experienced for each lens.
7. Replacement of one lens may present color problems. It is most advisable to replace both lenses in such cases.
8. Bifocals for exceedingly large lenses are not available. As previously stated one-piece bifocals are in very short supply. "Press-on" optics can be substituted.
9. Coating the lenses brown often changes the halides to act completely in the brown range.
10. At present most Photogray™ and Photosun™ lenses are in short supply. This writer spoke to Corning's representative at the Optical Fair '72 and was advised that additional molding facilities are being provided. However, the recent floods have literally inundated the entire plant. It will be some time before a return to normal operations will be effected.

*The writer should not make mention again, of the incalculable assist he gleaned from the text "Photochromatism" published by Wiley-Interscience a division of John Wiley & Sons, Inc., New York, London, etc. Book reviews are the province of another section of this journal. Hence, he will not mention, at this time, that those whose spirit moves them to additional investigative performance should, by all means, request having their name placed on the mailing list of this fine publisher of scientific books.

THE *Stoco* ASTIG GOGGLE

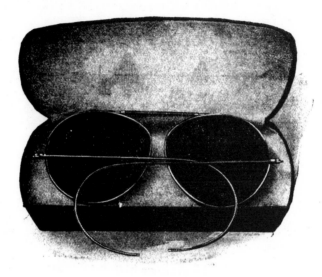

The *Stoco* Astig Goggle will fit any face perfectly and comfortably without any adjustment whatever. This is accomplished by the bar spring design and the form of the lenses which are so shaped as to follow closely the contour of the face. Your customers will appreciate the comfort and protection features of the *Stoco* Astig Goggle.

The frame including the Velvet Tip temples is 1-10 12 K gold filled throughout. The deeply curved 52 x 43 mm. coquille lenses are furnished in assorted shades of amber and fieuzal. Each Astig Goggle is packed in a good quality self-closing case.

Price........$24.00 per dozen

STANDARD OPTICAL CO.
Geneva, N. Y.

10 GLAZED GOODS

STORE BOUGHT

Glazed Goods" or "Readymades" are terms applied to a classification of spectacles and eyeglasses which have been manufactured for the sole purpose of being sold "over the counter" in so called five and dime stores. This type of eyewear is an outgrowth of the era of the itinerant spectacle vendor who would travel the countryside peddling his wares of "readymade" spectacles, whereas glazed goods were sold in the general store and the five and dime. In some instance the spectacle was brought to the patient. In the other the *patient* came to the store to select a *proper fit*.

The human anatomy, fortunately, is asymmetrical hence, the lens corrections most frequently could not possibly offer uniform results for both eyes. "Glazed Goods" or "Readymades" are produced with both lenses alike. The major run of foci are of a "spherical" form, not unlike a magnifying lens. No thought is given to the correction of astigmatism, near sightedness, eye-muscular imbalance or the usual asymmetric refractive error of the eye. Very few sets of eyes are alike. This difference is not accounted for in the manufacture of glazed goods. Nevertheless, enough of a substantial segment of the population both here and abroad overlook the possible immediate or long term harmful results and succumb to the cost advantage by shopping for a "good seeing pair of reading specs," in the five and dime store. The reader should be aware that selecting one's own ophthalmic correction is obviously an outgrowth and can probably be considered a procedure related to our ancestral heritage.

Primitive spectacles were self fitted or fitted with the aid of a crude trial set device, and a vendor whose knowledge of vision-care was most likely limited to what was gleaned from the fitting instructions accompanying the trial sets and sample kits. It was not until discoveries concerning the existence of the full range of refractive errors (and the instrumentation to diagnose these infirmities) that accurate prescriptions could be written for corrective lenses.

"Glazed Goods" are illegal in approximately 40 of the 50 United States. California is the "liberal healing cult state" where every legal and illegal quasimedical practitioner both of religious and non-religious conviction is permitted to exist and flourish. Here we accept herbal medicine, pseudo-medicine, para medicine, acupuncture, naturopathy, psychic mediums, faith healers, witchcraft, occultism, palmistry, Iridodiagnosis* and many more. It is the only state where the osteopathic physicians and surgeons, a most worthy healing faction, were legally handed a M.D. degree in 1962 without benefit of additional education by self-appointed degree donors. *If you can't beat them, join them.* At this writing the legality of this conversion is being tried in the courts. Some osteopaths refused the seemingly improved status purported to accompany this concerted union.

It is the opinions of the author that the newest Food and Drug Administration regulation which went into effect January 1972 will sharply curtail the sales of glazed goods. The additional expense involved in adding the compulsory safety factor to glass lenses may increase the selling price to where the existing difference may preclude their purchase. The FDA section 381, paragraph C, states that "in order to protect the public more adequately from potential eye injury, eyeglasses and sunglasses must be fitted with impact resistant lenses, except in those cases where the optometrist or physician finds that such lenses will not fulfill the visual requirements of the particular patient, and directs in writing the use of other lenses, and gives written notification thereof to the patient." England has required "safety lenses" for approximately ten years.

A great portion of glazed goods are made in rimless form which requires drilled holes in the glass. Some other mounting device must be developed or plastic lenses used in place of glass. The safety factor cannot be added to glass which contains holes. This too, will cause an increase in production cost and a possible retooling for the glazed goods manufacturer.

The sale of Glazed Goods was expanded considerably by

Plate 43

1. *Slipovers or grab front: Readymades to be used over regular distant glasses; yellow gold plated with magnifying lenses of 20" focus; circa 1920.*

2. *Readymade glazed goods with nearsighted non-astigmatic lens; rimless; all steel spring; circa 1900.*

3. *Same as #2 but more elaborate with handle, etc.*

4. *Readymade novelty type of folding small lorgnette with reading lenses; similar to ones made recently and imported from Japan; circa 1930.*

5. *Same as #4.*

6. *Readymade folding spectacles; zylonite; Japanese imports; fitted with reading lenses and often sold in novelty stores; circa 1930.*

7. *Same as #6 but folding zylonite lorgnettes. Really impressive but poor grade of both frame and lenses.*

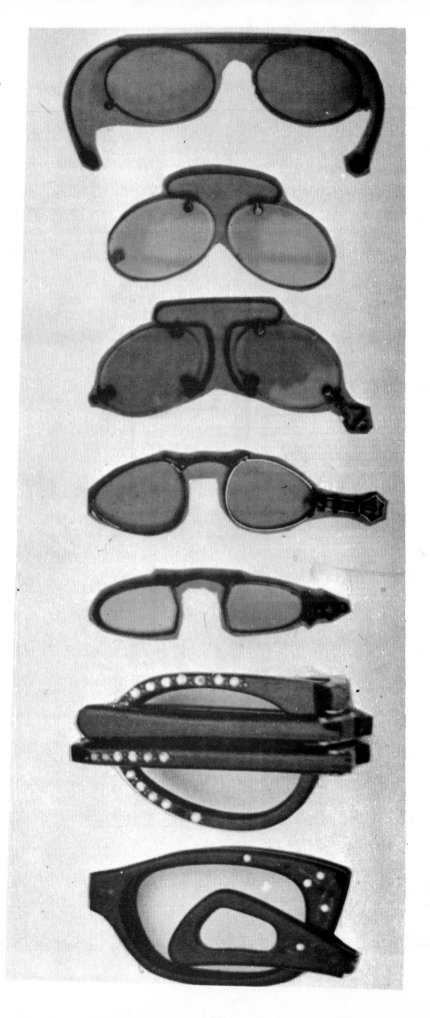

the introduction of Japanese imports of novelty specs in many categories. These are especially oriented for those requiring "reading glasses," and they are sold mainly in states permitting the vending of "glazed goods" and often passed illegally in the guise of novelties and notions. These are usually in the form of "halfeye*" in highly decorative zylonite or an imitation of the thin 1860 circa metal rim together with an aluminum carrying case. The price for these range from $3.00 to $15.00 and are sold over-the-counter in department stores or cut-price stores that handle assorted notions and home furnishings.

Some individuals may question the efficacy of a complete formal eye examination when all they may require is simply reading glasses (readymades) which they can still obtain at the five and dime. The answer has many aspects. The principal one deals with the focusing apparatus of the eye. In order for the eyes to see at different distances, the muscle of accommodation (the ciliary muscle) or the focusing apparatus must adjust the power of the lens in the eye (crystalline lens) to a more convex or lesser convex shape. The action of the ciliary is part of a reflex act. Two

other functions take place simultaneously, more simply, the focusing of the eye is a joint or communal function. Three responses occur at one time. 1) The focus a near object, the eye must converge to the point of fixation (turn-in). 2) The pupils must contract and 3) finally, the ciliary muscle must play on the lens in the eye and change its curve to the correct radius to see clearly. If any of the three functions are faulty the other two are affected accordingly. This may result in many eye anomalies. To name a few: doubling of vision, distended pupils, eccentric fixation (vision of one eye lessened because eye does not fixate on the central point of vision "fovea centralis"). This results in a slight deviation of one eye (slight cross-eye). Enough for this major reason.

To enumerate some of the other reasons for a complete eye examination:
1. To explore any potential eye or systemic diseases.
2. Check for Glaucoma* (measuring of intraocular pressure).
3. Orthoptic Training*
4. Correct binocular balance and stereopsis*
5. A.R.P.*

Motor car goggle from an advertisement early 20th century worn in (horseless buggy) open touring car.

Ralph Nader ... People's Advocate ... Where Are You?

... An Editorial

Most optometrists will query, "What concern has Ralph Nader with optometry?" It is now common knowledge that he has spoken-out against the flexible (soft-lens) contact lens. He has, on many occasions condemned the effective hierarchy of the AMA and since we are classified by the same AMA as an ancillary non-medical cult, we should similarly take heed to this blatant outspoken paladin. Indeed, Mr. Nader is a bold advocate fighting the cause of the people in their struggle to stem the forces of the evils of our chauvinistic bureaucracy, and the flagrant corporate miscarriage of ordinary business practices. This, a product of the latter's omnipotent control of every facet of the consumer's need.

The answer to this query can be assessed without any great measure of one's imagination if only we pause and take inventory of the multitude of flagrant abuses or the obscure inequities which plague our own profession. Here we act as the agent for those of the higher echelon of corporate industry in terms of our service to the consumer, the patient. It requires no special auditing ability to appreciate the prevailing device employed in the control of every activity germane to the ultimate level of *cost* and *quality* of optical commodities. This powerful ploy is vested not in the AMA or AOA or ADA or AOA (Osteopathic) but in shoddy corporate maneuvers, by delegating their paid underlings every phase of control from the raw material to what is dispensed to the patient (consumer).

The writer feels assured that his constituency, his readers, are appreciative of the tremendous impact made by Ralph Nader and his disciples since his crusade had its inception in 1965. Nevertheless, there are always those few who, for one reason or another, have failed to avail themselves of the existence of one, Ralph Nader, Nader's Raiders, and his principal functioning organization, (among others) The Center for Study of Responsive Law.

Ralph Nader is a Princeton-Harvard Magna Cum Laude Law Graduate of age 39, come February 27th. His parents were Lebanese immigrants who settled in Winsted, Connecticut, (A Rubicoff protectorate, a Nader ally) where his father Nadra Nader runs a restaurant, "to feed the body and mind" and to be the social focus for Winsted.

Ralph Nader has been called by many names ... Consumer advocate, the people's lawyer, Citizen Nader; the six-foot-four sad-eyed, shy, and slightly stooped Nader who could humble the all-powerful General Motors, a flamboyant crusader, a muckraker, amongst other endearing terms. Precisely a man whose primary purpose in life is to see the consumer get a "fair shake" ... and by the opposition ... as one prominent adversary replied when asked about Nader, and was quoted in THE WASHINGTONIAN magazine by writer Joseph Goulden as having said: ". . . him." This is but a mere inkling

'Flip-Up' Make-Up Glasses
• specially-created glasses to aid in the art of make-up . . . black plastic frames with individual flip-up eye-pieces (magnifying lenses for detail work)
pair. 3.99

Sampling of advertisement appearing in city newspapers.

of the many tirades proclaiming the intense provocation of the "powers to be."

It is not the purpose of this editorial to enter into a lengthy exposé of the state of the economy of the visual-care professions. This, the writer bequeaths to an optometric *ombudsman*, an *eye-raider*. However, for the moment, in an effort to stimulate an awaking, and "lest we forget," check off the following: 1) The regulation concerning corrected curve lenses. 2) This is the only country where another health-care organization employs lobbyists to hold-back progress in a so-called ancillary field using the guise of "practicing medicine" when any tool which will implement diagnosis should be permitted. Especially when without the use of this diagnostic tool, an estimated 70% of this work emanates from this *secondary profession*. Who suffers? Bravo! . . . Rhode Island. 3) Are the ready-made glasses and sunglasses sold over the counter in drug, department and sundry stores of corrected curve and impact resistant? The writer shopped a local general merchandise cut-rate store. He bought sunglasses at $1.99. The label stated "super lenses." It is true, the price was reduced but the lenses were not impact resistant and of coquille glass. The +0.75 readers were marked impact resistant. I am wondering if a flat lens can be of corrected curve despite it being hardened. The +4.00 boudoir make-up glasses were both non-impact resistant and not of corrected curve. (See illustration.) Do they have a special dispensation? . . . an exclusion?

The writer can go on indefinitely and offer many more abuses and inequities like the power of the FDA to create a virtual monopoly for seemingly preferred corporate interests. Is free enterprise dead? . . . "Today the large organization is lord and master and most of its employees have been desensitized, much as medieval peasants who never knew they were serfs" . . . Ralph Nader, in a speech to the Conference on Professional Responsibility, Washington, D.C.

Ralph Nader, where are you?   —L.D.B.

11

GROOVY EYEGLASSES

The author has previously referred to the advent of Groovy Eyeglasses. His feelings in that area were expressed to the optimum in a cover story he wrote which was published in April 1971 by the Optometric World, a monthly professional magazine. This article received considerable accolades and served as another stimulus toward his endeavor to explore and present his expertise relative to this exciting collectible. The article follows in its entirety:

Dr. Bronson 'digs' the young generation. "These young people are beautiful," he says.

The question may be asked, "What has brought about this drastic change in eyewear from the conventional or establishment type of plastic frame to the thin metal rim and rimless? What sequence of events has been responsible for this revolutionary changeover to groovy eyeglasses? The answer can have one or many facets. Words and phrases like rebellion, relating to, Renaissance, the In Thing, I Dig It, communicate with, and identify with, all enter into the formula of which the answer is composed.

I am aware that I could be numbered amongst the pioneers of the rebirth or is it parturition? Some five years ago, while my wife and I were waiting for our car to be brought to the front of a downtown hotel, where we had attended a dinner party, I stood adjacent to a meticulously dressed middle-aged woman who wore yellow gold thin metal rimmed frames which housed extremely high-focused myopic lenses. Her total appearance was so striking to one, like myself, attuned to cosmetically-appealing eyewear, that I was prompted to comment and inquire as to the origin of her spectacles. The wearer was elated with my remarks and revealed to me the identity of the British optical specialist who had custom made this one frame in accordance with the lady's design. She informed me that many people had stopped her and made favorable comments with respect to the unique appearance of her eyeglasses. She also mentioned that her thoughts were to design her glasses to resemble a "fun thing" rather than the staid, "visual aid to a life-long infirmity." She no longer gave the impression of being visually handicapped. The frame was restangular in shape and no more than 40 x 30 mms. in measurement with padded bridge. Her lenses were easily of -12.00 diopters. My enthusiasm was difficult to subdue.

The following morning, I composed a letter to my brother-in-law, who was a principal in a large eyewear importing establishment, with offices and showrooms on Fifth Avenue, in New York City. I explained my reactions to what I had witnessed, and included a rough sketch of the frame, I, also, inquired as to the feasibility of manufacturing such thin metal frames in a variety of shapes and sizes. What followed was lengthy long-distant phone conversations. These resulted in the production of a line of thin metal frames which were named after a famous 18th Century American who wore glasses

ROCK TRENDS — Some of the current forces in the music: Grand Funk Railroad, John Lennon, Elton John, Leon Russell and the Beach Boys.

Groovy glasses are for the "Rocks".

in addition to having contributed important developments to the ophthalmic field.

These metal frames were in five different shapes, namely, octagon, round, oval, rectangular, and diamond. All were 48 millimeter eyesize with a 20 mm. bridge and 5½ inch skull temples, and were manufactured for the Fifth Avenue firm by a New York metal house whose metal frame production was at a standstill since the advent of the so-called heavy shell frame, some 45 years ago (and who now claims "around-the-clock" production scheduled with six months delivery date).

The Fifth Avenue concern decided to glaze these frames with sun lenses. Their starting order was for ten thousand frames. They shipped sample kits to their accounts throughout the country. The acceptance of this new frame departure was so poor and the returns of these frame samples for refund so great that they were forced to "close-out" at a loss, selling their remaining stock to a Chicago cut-rate house.

It appeared that the new ethnic group rejected the frame glazed with the establishment type of gray lens. However, many did want the thin frame but fitted with their own prescription lens, coated or tinted in such groovy shades as blues, yellows, browns, reds, some shades of grey, green, and rose. The thin metal frames, especially the rounds and ovals, lent themselves to variations by re-shaping. From these five basic shapes sprung many more groovy shapes. The double aught eye, Ful-Vue metal type, aviator's goggle, rimless and thin tortoise were also an imposing factor of choice of selection by these new groups.

Several months later, to their dismay, the Fifth Avenue "entrepreneur" found themselves with orders for great quantities of TMR frames sans lenses, but the supply was no longer available. Buyers easily traced the source since the actual New York manufacturer was an old timer and about the only one remaining who stuck to what was left of the "metal findings" trade. Two experienced metal workers were his full complement of employees. These buyers quickly gobbled up his entire stock. His staff of workers now had been increased to a point where his sixty spot welding machines were again operational. The great mass of orders necessitated the production schedule of "around-the-clock." These spot welding machines are hard to come by. They are of a highly precision variety and are an important requirement for accuracy in gold welding for metal eyeglass work. The operators, too, must be highly skilled to produce acceptable work. The owner has been a friend of my family for at least fifty years. He confided to me that his principal problem is concerned with his constant search for satisfactory talent to operate these delicate machines. I have, also, seen the mail that he receives which is stacked high. Purchase orders for this new line of frames are received in such great quantities as to make it impractical to meet the demand. The TMR frame and its related stylings, rimless, Numonts, Rimways, sport-goggles, and thin shell frames have arrived and are here to stay for a long time. The highly decorative and ornamented heavy shell frames are being replaced by **simplicity.**

My personal experience, in my own practice, nonetheless, has been more fruitful. It is true that I was somewhat disappointed in the one size of 48E. I had planned on smaller sizes, and a variety of sizes. However, the metal house did produce several sizes and later two smaller; one oval and one rectangular, both with saddle bridges. Then, was added a 48E square frame. In my office, I had instructed my female assistant and stylist to show these newer frames, only after we had removed the sun lenses. This led to greater acceptance.

Three incidents followed, which, without a doubt, were the greatest stimulus to the demand for these frames, and established the trend in my locale, and undoubtedly permeating other sections of the country.

The first occurred some time after my introduction of the thin metal frame. A lady, accompanied by her teen-aged daughter, paid me a visit. I examined the mother while the daughter browsed around. The daughter excitedly barged into the examination room, and literally cried out that she must have the glasses in the shadow-box on the wall, in the reception room. I had displayed a double aught eye frame of about Civil War vintage. I told her it was not for sale. However, I mentioned to her that we had a box-full, in the basement of the family's New York optometric office. I wrote to my brother, who sent me about a dozen. The daughter was enthralled with the frame, and requested that I fit her own prescription into the rims.

I learned, later, that the young lady was a member of a folk-rock group. Within a week, all her co-musicians wanted similar frames, and even by the members of the group who did not need prescription lenses. This prompted a phone call to New York imploring my brother to mail me the balance of the old metal rims stowed away in the basement. He thought that I had lost my mind, since the postage would run to about $18.00, and he was apprehensive as to my ever realizing the mailing costs. The demand for these, also the rimless and the newer thin rims, spurted without limit. The referrals from the members of the group, alone, created a great demand. I could see that my paltry stock would vanish quickly. I placed an ad in the AOA News, offering hard cash for any old metal frames, used or unused. Quite a number of "old timers" responded, and my stock seemed to be temporarily replenished. I, also, wrote letters to all the former metal manufacturers for any stock that they may have hidden under some old bench. I met with some success and continued to replace my stock. Most manufacturers claimed that they had destroyed their old dies. Nevertheless, I felt quite secure in the supply, which was coming in. It was fairly obvious that there was a large underground market waiting to be tapped, here in the Los Angeles area.

This triggered the second incident. I took my problem of creating a demand to my marketing counsellor, my 15-year old daughter. "Check with the Los Angeles Free Press," was her advice. I phoned the Free Press, which was, at the time, a small Los Angeles underground paper (it now boasts a circulation of nearly 100,000) and was put in touch with a staff member. I explained that I had a quantity of these antique aught eye frames, and wondered how I could inform the then-called "hippy-group" of this. He was so excited in learning of this hidden cache that he said would be right down. He wanted a pair for himself. Within thirty minutes, he entered my office, and implored me to insert his prescription in one of these frames, insisting, though, upon bright red lenses for his special purpose. I knew that this could be accomplished with plastic lenses. When the glasses were dispensed, he was so thrilled

HEART SHAPED NOVELTY GLASSES DESIGNED ORIGINALLY BY THE AUTHOR. PHOTO FROM STAR.

STAR GIRL PATTY CLARK

PLACE THE FACE IN PEYTON PLACE

Los Angeles Herald-Examiner TV WEEKLY, May 19-25, 1968

that he promised to mention this in the next issue of the "Freep."

The Free Press of Los Angeles hits the stands on Thursdays, Friday and Saturday. I must have received 100 phone calls, followed by mail from all over the country, including the U.S. military in Vietnam.

The third event occurred immediately prior to July 26, 1968, a date I will long remember. I had examined a young lady who claimed that she had read about me in the "Freep." She questioned me as to what had provoked by interest in this new form of eyewear. I told her my story. She was quite interested, and told me that she would like me to meet her husband, who writes the "Wailing" column for the "Freep." The meeting with her husband apparently served as an interview, for the following week I received a phone call from him asking me to read his column for the week. It was necessary for me to go into town to obtain a copy, since the paper had not as yet been circulated in the "Valley." To my amazement, he had devoted an entire column to Dr. L. D. Bronson, Optometrist to the "love" generation. The acclamation that followed was unbelievable. My phone did not stop ringing. People were clamoring for my services. My waiting room was completely crowded from then on. If no seats were available, the floor served. My mere former staff of one receptionist increased to six. It became necessary for me to move to larger quarters. In addition to the increase in my practice, my life has been revitalized. These young people are beautiful. They do not mind waiting. The usual patient grievances are at a minimum and are easily and pleasantly resolved. I have learned to communicate with this group, which has been helpful to me in understanding my own teen-aged children.

It is true that I may have lost a few patients, members of the establishment, who cannot "dig" the group who now make up the major run of my patient load. Nevertheless, lately, even the parents are coming around to the advent of the "thin metal rim," and are frequenting my office.

At present, a week does not pass without a phone call from some optometrist, requesting that I supply them with information or some of my antiques. And now, too, all the major domestic and foreign frame manufacturers are in production of the metal frames. Only recently, the most staid establishment optical company ran a two-page ad in the optometric professional journals proclaiming their readiness to supply round eye saddle gold filled thin rimless frames.

At the very onset, requests usually referred to the frame, also, as the "John Lennon" type. Now, a further change. Requests are for frames like "Peter Fonda" in **Easy Rider,** or the type worn by members of the cast of "Mod Squad" or like the character in "Laugh-In" whose punch line is, "Verrydinter . . . resting." I can name a long list of prominent people in the public eye who are now part of the new generation and are identifying with people who are beautiful and active. The military, in Vietnam, or wherever, also, wish to abandon the "G.I." frame, a mark of repeated uniformity. They want to identify with these active groups, at home, or the people who symbolize peace, love, and freedom. By changing their frames to the "thin metal rim," they feel that they are identifying with something or someone, at home. "These G.I. frames just can't cut it."

My daily mail invariably includes two or three letters from all parts of this country, Canada, Alaska, Hawaii, and the U.S. naval and military forces. I want to believe that the advent of the changeover of frame styles symbolizes a step closer to Peace, Love, and Freedom.

Plate *44* portrays a number of prominent artists who are popular today. Their calling appears to be divided between screen talent and those of the "Rock" groups. It is apparent that their eyewear is an important identifiable part of their effective makeup. Their names follow: 1. John Lennon 2. Jennifer (Hair) 3. Bill Bixby 4. Arlo Guthrie 5. David Henesy (Oliver) 6. Ann-Margret-Roger Smith 7. Clarence Williams III 8. Charles Lloyd 9. Characteristic of a German wearing the monocle 10. Michael Cole 11. Peter Fonda 12. Tom and Dick Smothers 13. John B. Sebastian 14. Steve McQueen 15. Melody 16. Grace Slick 17. Roger McGuinn 18. Jerry Garcia and 19. Whose broken glasses?

The appeal of the newer groups for antique glasses has created an extreme scarcity of the authentic. In an effort to meet this demand the author has developed a method of antiquing presently produced metal frames. The pseudo-process was outlined in an article which follows: *The purpose is not to serve as a subterfuge but as a tool to enhance the appearance of the frame and improve its consumer appeal.*

Many prominent men in our history have been known and identified by the wearing of their glasses. A list of a few follows:

Douglas MacArthur	
(aviation goggles)	Franklin Roosevelt
George Bizet	Teddy Roosevelt
Winston Churchill	Charles Steinmetz
Banjamin Franklin	Leon Trotsky
Mahatma Gandhi	Woodrow Wilson
Count Toulouse Lautrec	Ed Wynn
Harold Lloyd	Emile Zola

If we view a group photograph of noted statesmen of the 18th century the absence of spectacle wearing would be conspicuous in comparison with a present day photograph of a like group. Probably half would be wearing eyeglasses and another percentage would have them in their pocket.

Plate 44

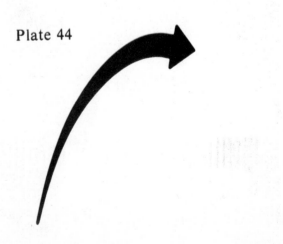

Simple Method of Antiquing and
Electroplating Metal Frames

Groovy Eyeglass, or thin metal rims, are presumably representative of an expression of emotional behaviorism germaine to the individualism of members of one facet of our present society.

This decade is witnessing a fragmentation of our society, a separation of social caste. The "establishment" versus such orders as the "Hippies, Black Panthers, Weathermen, Women's Lib and an assortment of ethnic groups — a new society disjointment.

The so called "Hippy" groups embrace a movement which foster, as part of its tenets; a complete rebellion against the accepted apparel of the day. The dress is either authentic Colonial or a very excellent replica. The long flowing, high necked gown embellishes the female or else the "close to the earth attire" of shopworn and profusely patched blue-jeans for both male and female of the species, to the bare feet or heavy work shoes, Colonial hats, burlap handbags, tie-dyed undershirts and even to natural birth. Anything which could be termed rebellious or relating to what is considered a better era, a remnant of the "good old days."

A similar attitude pervades the field of eyewear. These new ethnic groups take to antique spectacles. If these spectacle frames are not to be obtained from their vision specialist they turn to the local antique emporium of boutique shop or else scour the flea markets or swap meets. If luck has it grandma's attic relinquishes another art treasure in the form of her old specs.

The author is confident that the vision-care professions have been made aware of the tremendous sociological impact promulgated by these new groups to the extent that even the most establishment of the population is bending to the new horizons advanced by the "hip generation". The "older folk" are also taking to thin metal rims, et al. The World War II veteran retrieves his old "gas mask frames," that is, if his son, daughter or grandchildren did not get to them first.

Fortunately, many variations of this type of eyewear have been revived from the starting point of Hudson's Hullabaloo. Yellow, silver, black pewter, antique bronze, antique green gold are but a few metal platings and enameling now being spewed out from the color caldrom.

The ophthalmic dispenser, at present, must be mindful of these changes so that he remain at tune to the demands of the style conscious patient. The importance of a proper appearing visual appliance is part of the armamentum of the successful practitioner (see Dr. Dowaliby "Cosmetic Dispenser")

Photo shows more extensive lab which includes two small rectifiers.

Many practitioners have divorced themselves completely from all matters relevant to lab work. However, there are those who, for numerous reasons, feel moved to include this mechanical phase of the work. Of course, this practitioner is required to have available complete sample assortments of metal frame stylings, which include metal in colors.

The author has developed a simple method of electroplating frames using dry cell batteries. Of course, a small 6 volt 10 amp rectifier which is used by some jewelers, will be more substantial, nevertheless the batteries serve the purpose quite efficiently.

The electroplating process involves the transfer of ions from a metal electrode, the anode (plus pole), to an electrode, the cathode (minus pole) which is the object to be plated. The cathode is submerged in an electrolytic cell which contains ions of various substance. The process is activated by the application of a low voltage direct current. The electrolyte or fluid used for the transfer usually contains a small amount of acid plus an aqueous solution which makes it conductive. In some instances low heat may be required in order to accelerate the transfer.

The apparatus used is basic. It consists of a 1½ volt dry cell general purpose battery usually costing $1.50 each, a variety of ready-to-use solutions, a metal anode, several polyethylene containers and some pre-cleaning solution such as the one described later, a thermometer, a heating device, either a small calrod electric stove or a submergible heater as used to heat a tropical fish tank. (see diagram)

Supplies can be purchased from any plating equipment or commercial chemical house. It is more

Plate 45

1. *Spectacle: present day reproduction of round metal frames in common usage from 1940 to days of the Pilgrims. Round, yellow, gold-filled skull temples.*

2. *Spectacle: same as 1 but rectangle.*

3. *Spectacle: same as 1 but oval.*

4. *Spectacle: same as 1 but octogan.*

5. *Spectacle: same as 1 but halfeye.*

6. *Spectacle: same as 1 but freeform.*

7. *Spectacle: same as 1 but air corp goggle.*

8. *Spectacle: same as 1 but heavy duty V wire called X15; one of the most popular models. Lenses are quite large, 58mm across. Glass safety lenses are non-indicative because of weight factor. Plastic lenses are the "in thing" (Out of the dark).*

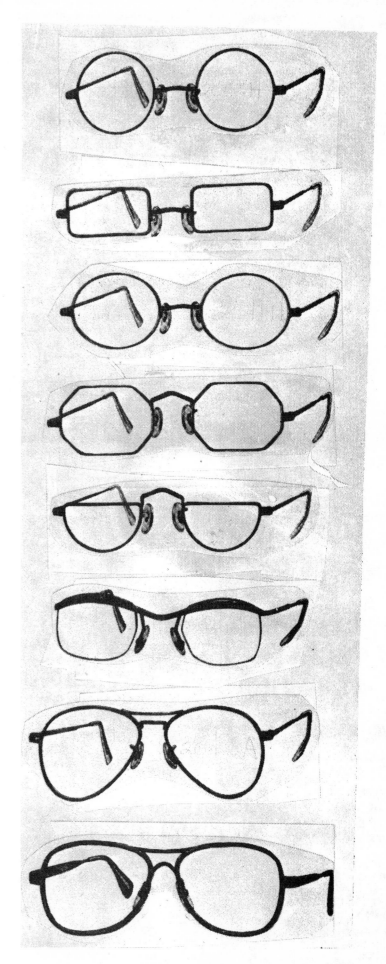

economical, however to purchase the small quantities required for single frame plating from a plater of small parts like Groovy Eyeglass Co., in Studio City, California. Instructions for specific colors are supplied.

The following are the requirements for the most frequently used metalic dispositions.

Color	Metal Anode	Ready to use Solution	Remarks, Special Requirements
Copper & Antique Copper	copper	Copper	Easily performed at room temperature also for antiquing. 1½-3 volts current.
Black Gray Antique Gray	stainless steel chromium (lead) nickel	Electroblack Chrome Black Black Nickel	Pre-copper plate required and heat 138° F C = 3 volts.
Silver Silver Matte	silver	Special brilliant silver-lume	Small quantities available only from Groovy Eyeglass Co. Room temperature C = 1½ volt.
Gold Yellow Green	stainless steel or gold	Gold	Variety of colors dependent upon heat & cycle C = 1½ volt.
Antique Black	nickel	Nickel	Heat required. Degree of deposit variable. C = 3 volts.
Chrome	lead	Chromic & Sulphuric Acid	Not recommended for small users.

C = Current density.

Other formulae can be similarily prepared. One of the most critical steps in the process is to be certain the material to be plated is absolutely, spotlessly clean. All finger marks and other defects will deter plating. It is advisable even to buff-polish a frame prior to plating.

The battery set-up can serve a dual purpose, i.e., to clean and sterilize all metal frames, in particular those to be plated. This method is recommended in preference to the ultrasonic type of agitator (see diagram) and used successfully as an adjunct to dispensing. Operated at room temperature or slight heat for 30 seconds using 3 - 6 volts.

Most present dry cell batteries are self rechargeable when not in use.

The results obtained using the described method will be gratifying and lend itself to greater diversification in frame coloring. The author will be happy to supply additional information by mail.

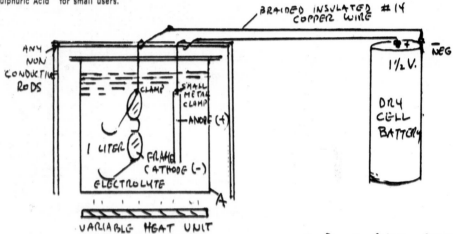

A = TANK CAN BE PURCHASED IN FOOD MARKET SAME AS USED FOR REFRIGERATOR STORAGE. LID NECESSARY TO PREVENT EVAPORATION WHEN NOT IN USE

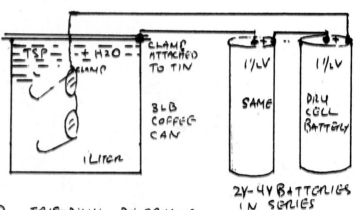

TSP TRISODIUM PHOSPHATE PLUS WATER IS THE ELECTROLYTE

Time Out For Hobbies

● It's difficult at times to believe that the people who act in daytime serials can lead lives far less complicated than those of the people they portray on television. Herewith, proof that life — off camera — is not all filled with problems and sorrows for members of the cast of NBC's Days of Our Lives. The continuing stars have a variety of interests to pursue at their leisure, including everything from collecting spectacles to a bird watching hobby.

Macdonald Carey, star of the series, while off-duty enjoys a game of chess.

Frances Reid, Carey's wife in the series, is something of a bird fancier.

And here we have Marie Cheatham (she's Marie), a spectacle collector.

Regina Gleason, featured in role of Kitty, works on some antiques.

Above, Denise Alexander, who plays Susan, likes decorating. Left, Coleen Gray, Susan's mother in series, has variety of pets. K. T. Stevens, who portrays Helen, has a hobby of amateur horticulture.

12

RING

ON YOUR FINGER *

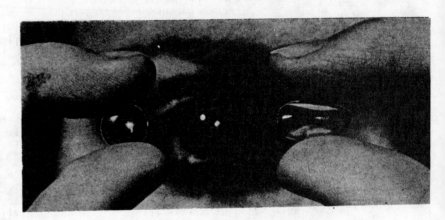

It may appear incredible to the reader that Leonardo da Vinci* one of the great creators during the Renaissance Period (1508) sketched and described the first contact lens. Although his method of application was quite involved, the principle was not unlike our present day conventional type of hard plastic corneal contact lens.

Over a century later Rene Descartes, who wrote extensively on ophthalmic subjects, also described a form of contact lens. Three centuries later (about 1887) the actual application of a glass shell was made on a human eye.

F. A. Muller, who made artificial eyes, can be given credit for the first fitted form of contact lens. It was a therapeutic type, used primarily to protect the cornea when the eyelids did not close completely; or when a separation of the lids from the cornea was indicated in cases where the lid was infested with a contagious bacterial organism such as is found in Trachoma. This insidious disease was quite prevalent in Europe at the turn of the century. By separating the lid from the cornea the latter was spared the insult of the disease organism. Blindness was a common result from such a transfer of infectious bacteria.

There were many more attempts to perfect some form of transparent shell application to correct corneal irregularities, abnormalities or malformations, (Kerataconus*). All attempts met with a variance of success. Wherever glass was used for the purpose, both the tolerance factor and visual acuity were beyond human endurance. A two hour wearing period was the limit, with cloudy vision most of the time.

The greatest impetus to the posture of contact lens potential was the development of a transparent plastic polymethyl methacrylate, (trade names Lucite, and Plexiglass)

followed by polymers of polyesters. The one single property of plastic which served the greatest advantage was the reduced weight factor, followed by the ability to lathe the lenses to precision tolerances and microthickness without altering its consistent structural uniformity.

Many investigators, developers, experimenters, and outright inventors who worked with the lens were responsible for continuous progress in an effort to approach its practical present state. To name a few: W. Kalt, William Feinbloom, John Mullen, Theodore Obrig, Norman Bier, Frank Dickenson, Kevin Tuohy, Wilhelm Sohngis, and many other pioneers.

In 1957 John de Carle of England patented a bifocal contact lens and so did Newton Wesley of Chicago in 1958.

In 1961 several Czech scientists experimented with hydrophil.ic plastic and developed this to be used as a contact lens material.

Bausch and Lomb reputedly spent 3.3 million dollars developing a method of producing and perfecting this hydrophylic material. In 1971 the Pure Food and Drug Administration approved their lens for human application.

The author has fitted the "soflens," as it is called in over 100 patients. He can safely say this form of "membrane optics" is unbelievable. It fits over the entire cornea, hardly moves, is impossible to detect and is so comfortable that the immediate response from the wearer is "phenomenal, incredible, sensational". It completely outranks the conventional hard type of corneal lens. The problems encountered by today's 10 million wearers of the hard type has caused approximately one-third to store these away in a drawer and return to the wearing of the now "in" or "groovy eyeglasses." This latter one-third group is the principal subject for the new soft contacts. Obviously, as with all new applications for visual betterment, the lens has some shortcomings. Complete details appeared in an article written by this author and follows:

A Non-Academician's Report on the Fitting of the Soft Contact Lens

In deference to what is commonly thought to be the major shortcoming in the fitting of the most recent adjunct to the armamentum of devices which serve to correct vision discrepancies. to wit: membrane optics. soft contact lenses. silicone contact lenses, it has become painfully apparent that the real culprit is not the potential danger of possible invasion by some insidious bacterial organism. or the insult of edema. The primary disparity involves the simple resolution of satisfactory and continuously comfortable visual acuity.

In addition and coincidental with the advent of membrane optics (apparently. this nomenclature has been adopted by the Academy to describe the several forms of contact lens of a softer texture and microthin). both the profession and the laity have found themselves embroiled in a continuous stream of adverse public notoriety which has remained practically unrefuted. This condition has resulted in fostering a feel of apprehension especially with the professional who has not as yet added the fitting of this new form of optics to his scheme of services. Both the patient and professional appeal has become somewhat of a question. The non-fitting doctor* has rightfully stressed these inequities when questioned by a prospective candidate. thus. adding to the confusion. The patient's acceptance has been affected to a point whereby an attitude of "laissez faire" or "I'll wait until perfected". has fully consumed his motivation. This apprehensive feeling has prevaded also those early or naive wearers of the soft contacts and set-up a situation of justifiable doubt and discontentment.

Prior to the introduction of soft lenses the author was fitting an average of twenty conventional lenses per month. followed by the accepted ratio of successful cases. Obviously. he showed great interest at the instance of introduction of the new lens. Hence. he was among the first to attend the "one day seminars in the correct fitting procedure". where he was both indoctrinated and brainwashed by the detail men. His first experiences were gleaned from the first "softees" which had not as yet been approved. This was followed by the purchase of a complete trial set of the approved type: and later by a sampling of the silicone product.

The author has mentioned previously that his average monthly fitting of conventional contacts totaled about twenty. In addition his expertise activities in

*Refers to Doctors without **legal** soft lens trial sets.

the vision-care field has extended over a period of more than thirty years. His efforts with other phases of transparent plastics have resulted in many advantages ibid pages 7 through 10 Introduction to article Optometric World Dec. 1971.

The author can now quote from his own office files with respect to his experience with this new form of optics. Since April of 1971 to March 1972, he has fitted a total of one hundred pair of "Softees". Approximately thirty pair of an unapproved type (C) and twenty pair of a silicone type construction (A). The third. an approved type (B) will be considered anon. An analysis of these must be representative or a close approximation of the experiences encountered by other average practitioners. This may serve also as a basis for future expecteds unless embellished by later refinements.

The thirty type C were lathe ground and polished from the polymer prior to hydration. This method provides good optics. These were supplied in several overall diameters. radii of curvature and the full range of foci. 1) Their principal fault lies in the instability of the material with respect to the diameter. Apparently this is due to the coefficient of absorbtion of the hydrating solution. Very few practitioners are exacting chemists. 2) The requirement of mobility is impractical. Movement of the lens is experienced by a large percentage of those fitted. This situation may become a hazard when quick eye rotation is required in driving an automobile— a sudden drop of visual acuity is experienced. 3) These lenses rip or tear easily. They crack on the patient's eye and fray at the edges. 4) Their percentage of fluid content is such that the O.D. is easily altered by a variation of it's isotonicity.

Decentralization of the lens creats some visual disturbance. but nowhere the distortion as experienced in type (B). which is a spin-cast lens and worked so that outside of the central 4 to 5 millimeters is spherical. while the remaining parameter is aspherical.

The twenty type (A) are prepared from silicone. a synthetic resin. The construction design is such that a minimum center thickness is required. This makes them too thick for common usage. There wearing quality offers little advantage over the conventional hard type for its pliability. It is not as soft or thin as the hydrophoric type of soft lens. Nineteen of the twenty patients fitted with this type could not find any appreciable difference or greater comfort than that offered by the wearing of the conventional hard type. The one who could wear the A type was age 54 inclined to act like age 34. Her lids, both upper and lower were exceptionally flabby. This latter characteristic may account for her being able to tolerate this type in comfort.

The B type is the approved one. The author has evaluated his results by presenting a list of conditions. The patient's immediate reaction to its comfort giving faculty is excellent. It can be considered absolutely invisible. Patients who can be fitted and who obtain sufficient visual acuity to suit their requirements feel quite happy wearing them. Some small segment, wear these for special occasions and are given to understand their shortcomings. There are those who cannot possibly wear the conventional type, and who will tolerate the soft ones, notwithstanding the relative loss in acuity. However, the conditions of their employment preclude the wearing of glasses (cocktail waitress - flight attendants, Playboy bunnies, certain sports, etc.).

These are the conditions:

Condition #1 If the Doctor can subdue his sense of responsibility to the patient — and the patient (a proper candidate) is willing to accept a loss of visual acuity of anywhere up to 50% on the Snellen Chart.

Condition #2 (The doctor's obligation remains static.) If the patient is willing to risk potential hazard in driving.

Condition #3 If the patient is willing to overlook the consequences of transitory dehydration when entering a normally air-conditioned room or a windy atmosphere.

Condition #4 If the patient is willing to guarantee a continuous and full flow of lacrimal fluid.

Condition #5 If the patient is willing to serve as an involuntary human guinea pig.

Condition #6 If the patient is given to understand that physical changes in molecular structure of the lens can occur if worn continuously for six months; notwithstanding insult to the cornea.

Condition #7 If the patient is given to understand that in many cases a loss of accommodation is evident.

Condition #8 If the patient is given to understand that the wearing of soft contacts can create an extra ocular muscle imbalance, spatial disparity; barrel distortion. These are but a mere semblance of the possible inequities encountered by the patient. Now for the Dr.

Condition #9 If the doctor is willing to understand that extra care should be exerted in selection of a **proper candidate.** There are too many No!, No's! (restrictions)

Condition #10 If the doctor will forget what has been professed as a truism by the detail men, (manufacturer's reps.), (In medical jargon "pill pushers") that an arbitrary 1.50 diopter of astigmatism can be resolved; be it, subjective ast., objective ast., corneal ast., lenticular ast., or residual ast. This is a gross misrepresentation. In actual practice a .50 D astigmatism, especially against the rule, is enough to create a visual loss of up to 50%.

Condition #11 If the doctor will consider that a movement of only 1 millimeter off center will create a blur so that the 20/400 line appears distorted.

Condition #12 If the doctor will understand that in too many cases of a perfect spherical refractive error of O.U.-2.00 and corrected with spectacles to 20/20 in each eye, with "softees" vision will be clear in one eye and blurred with the other or blurred in both eyes. Transfer of lenses from one eye to the other will prove that the eye with lowered visual acuity will remain, "status quo". Do not seek an explanation!

Condition #12A If the doctor understands that the lenses of identical diameter and curvature are not within tolerance sufficiently to be interchangeable, when replacement is needed as a result of loss.

Condition #13 If the doctor will understand that increasing the power by a -1.00 D.S. in an effort to bring about a better fit is not correct refractive procedure. The detail men arbitrarily advise such an increase. This method only proves their lack of knowledge with respect to refraction. The writer has indeed wondered how many soft lenses were fitted by the lecturing detail men to afford them a special license to alter basic refractive procedure?

Condition #14 If the doctor will understand that correctly fitted lenses will often shift laterally on the corneal area and often remain in this position. This will create a loss of vision.

Condition #15 If the doctor will understand that stability of lens position is dependent upon the anatomical structure and resultant action of the upper lid. Tightness of the lid will tend to lift the lens not unlike that of the conventional type.

If these conditions are understood thoroughly then proceed with the fitting of soft contact lens.

The writer has studied and appraised these conditions carefully. As a result several departures from the staid procedure have evolved. One in particular follows — a patient complained of loose lenses. He asked him if his saline solution was correctly prepared. The patient could not remember if he had added the salt tablet. The writer told him to dissolve another tablet. He called me back shortly and said his lenses are nice and snug for the **first time.** Making the lenses hypertonic may solve the problem of loose lenses.

What would it take to make the lacrymal fluid continuously hypertonic?

The writer has suggested an additional series. The only available alternative to improve the fit is by a variance of the focal power i.e. increase the steepness by an increase of the minus and vice versa.

It should be clearly understood that the purpose of the foregoing is not to dissuade the practitioner from becoming involved with the soft contact lens. On the contrary, the reverse is more applicable. The writer remembers the problems encountered when the large glass Zeiss scleral type was introduced in America . . . and the metamorphosis that ensued.

Very recently E. I. du Pont de Nemours & Co. disclosed that it was engaged in the development of a material for a contact lens. The material is described as hard, yet supple — not soft or hydrophylic. The plastic is also oxygen-permeable. This characteristic is not unique since the silicone material possesses a like quality. The DuPont material, because of its hardness, does not absorb moisture, hence, bacterial contamination would not be encountered. The advantages over present material for contact lenses is not as yet available. Assuredly, their's must have something different. Large interests do not expend efforts to no or little avail.

SLEEP — THRU OPTICAL

. . . An Editorial — *a likely foible*

Once upon a time a California Optometrist and his wife went for a stroll before dinner on the main drag of this middle-class residential community. They passed a street level professional office obviously of recent occupancy and noted a sign lettered on the window which read **SLEEP-THRU OPTICAL**. The optometrist, Dr. O, a 30 year man, queried of his wife, "I wonder what kind of a new optical thing is this?" "I believe I know all the optical companies around" (You see, he read all the ads in all the journals) "I cannot recall ever seeing the name." The Doctor was an inquisitive soul. He edged over to the door and dared a peek inwardly. There he perceived a man busy at a desk and a chic young lady, thirty-fivish in full regalia, dark tailored skirt and white professional jacket, only the stethescope was missing; the mm rule and occluder clearly visible from her upper left-hand **breast** pocket. No! she was not holding an ophthalmoscope.

It was exactly 6:00 P.M. The man at the desk promptly rose and walked to the front door apparently to "close-up shop". The sign, "parking in the rear" told the story for the others. This happened at the instance Dr. O was ogling the interior. Their eyes met. Obviously inquisitive, the man opened the door as if readying to leave. Dr. O spoke first, "I am Dr. O, a local optometrist, I was just wondering what product you sell? Your company name seems to evade my memory", "Oh! I am Mr. N. I fit the revolutionary **SLEEP-THRU** contact lens. The one which can be worn continuously without removing during sleeping hours. It can be worn for a week or more at a time." Dr. O mentioned that he had had inquiries from a few of his patients regarding these. They had seen the ads. This had prompted him to phone the lab where they are made. He had spoken to the man who claimed to be the original developer of the lens, a Mr. D. Mr. D bemoaned the fact that he had unwittingly franchised the entire L.A. area exclusively to a dispensing optician and had thrown in Orange County to clinch the deal. Orange County is Dr. O's home base. Mr. D continued and explained the only procedure left for Dr. O was to write a prescription for lenses and send it with the patient to the franchised optician who in turn will have an ophthalmologist verify the prescription *since it is illegal for an optician to fill a prescription written by an optometrist*. The optician will then take additional measurements with the Locometer* and complete the fitting of the "Sleep-thru Contact Lenses" with the aid of fluorescene strips and black light which the optometrist is not allowed to use. Furthermore, the ophthalmologist can be consulted in the event the lenses cause problems which require additional medicants. Mr. D implied, in no small talk, that he works exclusive-

ly with ophthalmologists who are the only professionals permitted to use the Slit-Lamp, being this instrument is employed solely to diagnose diseases and often needed to verify a contact lens fit. This was the abrupt sum-total of the phone conversation.

The impromptu meeting between Dr. O and Mr. N. appeared to evince the status of "a gift of great munificence." Mr. N invited the Doctor and his wife to visit with him. The befrocked lady and other personnel had already left for the day.

Dr. O and his wife were ushered into the reception room which was in keeping with the poshness of Beverly Hills . . . deep piled rugs . . . and other appointments showing evidence of the skill of considered interior embellishment . . . It exuded the dignity of a well organized professional office. Mr. N. seated himself behind the massive desk and motioned to his visitors to follow his lead and use the adjacent seats facing him. The Doctor noted as he entered that the center table was laden with a variety of brochures obviously proclaiming the virtues of the **SLEEP-THRU** contact lens.

Indeed, here was located the exclusive franchised office for Orange County. Mr. N had revealed to Dr. O that he had purchased this exclusivity from the holder of the L.A. franchise for a large sum of money and that he had spent an additional $20,000 in furnishing the office plus some more thousands for the equipment which included (and was visable from this vantage point) an automated refracting chair, a Burton blue light, fluorescene strips, a B. & L. Keratometer with Locometer* attachment, a B. & L. Vertometer, an A.O. giant size Radiuscope (Drysdale method), a set of binocular flip trial lenses (with handles) and an array of assorted contact lens solutions which certainly include the astringents, the alkoloids (ephedrine) the antihistamines (ophthalmic) and even Visine, 20/20 eye drops, and Clear Eyes. Of course, these were only in sample form. The regular size must be purchased at the pharmacy (none attached to the premises).

The purpose of the cordial hospitality soon became evident; to wit, Dr. O was obviously interested in this intriguing bonanza and Mr. N had a *problem*. Mr. N began with his willingness to elaborate on the merits of this incredible **SLEEP-THRU** Contact Lens which "is destined to displace all forms of contact lenses including the very controvertial Soflens (TM). It was the Doctor's immediate conviction that with a man of Mr. N's calibre at the helm of such a franchising organization, the contact lens section of optometry could very well be abduced. In this short elapsed time period Dr. O was fully impressed with Mr. N's intrepid and indefatigable capabilities in the area of business acumen. For, as he explained, prior to his purchase of this franchise, had he not sold his wholesale lettuce business (refurbishing lettuce *seconds* so that they could be sold as *firsts*) for the round sum of $150,000.00 in cash, when his original investment was a paltry $40,000.00? He had considered the franchise investment as a ploy or tax shelter manipulation when the annual IRS auditing time arrives. He had never thought it would turn out to be such "easy pickin's".

Now, Mr. N felt he was making his point. He paused to show the Doctor that in the nine weeks since commencing this practice of dispensing **SLEEP-THRU** Contacts, he had already completed 58 cases. "These lenses are the *greatest*." "Of course, I am only a promoter, you know, the business head." "This is a push-over". "I charge $250.00 per pair (cash only). "I get the lenses from Mr. D's lab at $35.00". "I hired a female optician who does all the measuring and fitting. She works on a straight salary and commission which commensurates with her ability to complete as many as possible in the shortest time possible. This represents an incentive for her to sell an extra pair."

Dr. O who obviously feinted as being enthralled by this fantastic experience, however unrealistic it appeared, edged a little closer to the scene of operation, the fitting room. He was an inquisitive sole, as was stated previously. He casually scanned the wall areas making certain he covered all possible terrain. Yes! right on! No signs of a certificate, permit, license or registration of any kind on display. This prompted a question. "Is your optician licensed?" His reply was definite and immediate. "An optician is not required to be licensed."

Now, we have arrived at the "nitty gritty' of the "whole thing". It appears that Mr. N. was worried. He had plunged into this bountiful "Horn o' plenty" without prior investigation. He was now worried, **"Am I Legal."**

The end of this phantasmagoria.

The following are statements of facts taken from formal legal records and whatever:

1) There are 18 institutes of learning offering courses in opticianry, of these 7 have two year college courses. Los Angeles City College is one. At the beginning of this semester a question arose regarding the feasibility of the course being given this year, since those registered numbered only 13. A mere 9 appeared at the first session and the minimum attendance requirement would be in the area of 20. After the first session Dr. John Archer, the instructor feels fully rewarded if 4 show up. This happens in the night session. The day session is favored with much better attendance.

2) No person other than a physician and surgeon or optometrist may *measure the powers* or range of human vision or determine the accommodative and refractive status of the human eye or the scope of its functions in general or prescribe ophthalmic or *contact lenses.*

3) Opticians are licensed in the following states: Arizona, California, Connecticut, Florida, Georgia, Hawaii, Kentucky, Massachusetts, Nevada, New Jersey, New York, North Carolina, Rhode Island, South Carolina, Tennessee, Virginia, Washington. Requirements vary with each state.

The following are also facts in evidence of common practice:

1) An optician need not have completed a High School education.

2) The larger multiple dispensing operations have been known to elevate a stock clerk, with no prior formal education, to the position of dispensing optician.

3) Any owner-operated dispensing establishment, without hesitation, will duplicate a corrective lens without prescription.

4) Opticians who fit contact lenses will measure the corneal radii with the Keratometer irrespective of the ruling requiring the presence of the physician or optometrist.

5) The writer knows of a case where a clerical employee in a hospital optical dispensary was handed registration by simply fulfilling the fee requirement of $50.00. It is true this was an emergency, *the regular optician "split".*

CONCLUSION . . . What to do? You name it!

* A device designed by Mr. D which is attached to a Keratometer and contributes to charting the topography of the cornea at quadrantal divisions.

WAILING NAT FREEDLAND

Would you believe a measly two—column inch ad in the Freep could be worth ten grand and revitalize your life?

I was buying my old lady some groovy, antique wire—rimmed glasses for her birthday — as advertised in the Freep — and got the whole inspiring story from Dr. Louis D. Bronson, Optometrist to the Love Generation.

"I thought of myself as a red—hot Marxist when I was going to college in New York,"says L.D. "And when I studied painting I was around the Greenwich Villiage crowd all the time. But you know how it is, you get responsibilities with family and business and as the years go by you start to lose your zip and feel out of things."

The 1946 optometry certification on the wall of his Sherman Oaks office shows an L.D. Bronson with slicked—back hair, a bowtie and a white sportjacket with a hankie in the breastpocket. These days he looks a lot more youthful, despite maybe 25 added pounds and grey hair. He's into a brushed—forward mod coiffure and wears some of his own best grandpa glasses. Copies of the F.P. are prominently displayed in his waiting room and may be taken off free by any Valleyite who needs turning on.

He digs going to Love—Ins with his teenage daughter, had a display at the Renaissance Faire, sat in on KPPC strike meetings and is putting his glass—cutting expertese to work in some fine far—out stained glass bas reliefs. "I'm a new man,"he says, bustling around from one project to another. "I feel twenty years younger. I really like what's going on with the kids today."

It started about two years ago when a lady came in with her teen daughter who was in a folk—rock group. Just for kicks, Bronson had a century—old pair of steel frame glasses he had somehow come up with via his family's optometry tradition. "I must have these,"said the chick. "They're boss."

"These glasses aren't for sale,"said L.D. "I could never find another like them. But I know we have a whole box of the same type of frame down in the cellar of my father's old optometry office back in New York. I could have a couple of pairs sent out here."

Which he did. And then the chick's whole group wanted matching shades, even the members who didn't need prescriptions. This required cleaning out the cellar back east and a shipping charge of $1. "I hoped I'd get the mail costs back," Bronson said. "But then all these kids sent their friends in for wire frames and the whole supply was cleaned out."

So he had to get some more, which he did by putting an ad in the optometrists' professional journal offering hard cash for any old metal frame eye-men had lying around. He had been checking the big frame companies and asking them to run off a few orders for him, but their metal frame molds were thrown away long ago.

But anyhow, a supply was coming in again and it was fairly obvious there was some kind of a big underground market here, waiting to be tapped. So Bronson took the problem to a local youth marketing expert, his 17—year—old daughter. "Take an ad in the Free Press," was her advice.

The first week the ad appeared he got fifty appointments and mail orders for hippie glasses. "Keep the ad in,"he ordered. Business has leveled off nicely at 30 orders a week. A lot of the work comes in by mail and one of the biggest market areas is U.S. military in Vietnam. Our heads in uniform seem to want some sort of symbol to identify themselves to other reluctant warriors.

All this has put an extra $10,-000 in his annual income. "But the best part of it all is the beautiful people I meet", says L.D. "They're really so alive and interesting. So much nicer than my straight customers. Older, up-tight people are always trying to walk out with glasses and telling me to bill them later, or they yell and scream if the work gets delayed. There was this geology teacher at Caltech who lived up in the mountains in a cottage without a phone. He and his wife drove all the way to Van Nuys Bou-

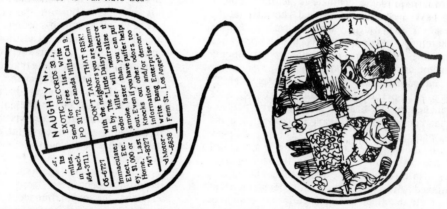

levard three Saturdays in a row when my laboratory fouled up the order. They never complained, they said it was a nice drive. I have found that flower children types never break appointments and never try to cheat you out of payment."

Just before, a kid with a goatee and long hair had told him he didn't think he'd have the bread for a pair of specs in time for the delivery date. "We'll just hold them till you can come in," said Bronson. "Don't worry."

Naturally, he lost a few customers under the new regime. "There was one of my old patients who drove up in his Rolls—Royce one day and got very angry when he saw the Free Press in the waiting room. I asked him if he ever read the paper before and he said no. So I told him he'd better take home this copy and read it before he calls it dirty and filthy again. He never came back to my office after that."

By now, all the main eyeglass frame factories have gotten tooled up for wire—rims. But they're way behind an old manufacturer in Long Island City who had been struggling to stay alive until the fad came back bigger than ever. "This was a man who really believed in metal frames and he could never put his heart into making the tortoise—shell plastics. I found out about him just in the nick of time. He's a month behind all his orders now, but he still gives me my wire-rim frames at the lowest jobber price."

Granny glass lovers have been vindicated after the long harsh years. Even Europe is now into producing genuine "John Lennon Glasses."

151

13

EYE TEST EXPLAINED

The reader may question the relevance of explanatory notes concerning routine eye examinations as performed by all practitioners in the present day vision-care professions. The author believes this to be pertinent on two counts. First, to evidence the tremendous progress in the ophthalmic healing professions in the past century, and second, because of the concerted requests so frequently made by patients having their eyes examined, and left literally *in the dark* when confronted by the mountains of complex instruments used by the doctor during the examination.

Since the introduction of "Third party payment*" which benefit a vast percentage of recipients of services from all branches of the healing and ancillary professions, there has been an extraordinary increase in demand for services, especially of the doctor. The practitioner is seldom inclined or has the time to explain in any detail the function and value of the elaborate instrumentation needed to perform a routine eye examination. The patient is duly dismissed with only a cursory understanding of the meaning of all the findings. In an effort to enlighten those so inclined, the following is representative of an explanation of a routine eye examination.

There are three principal methods of determining the refractive* status of the eye. The mechanics of vision is such that the ciliary muscle in the eye or the muscle which controls the focusing ability of the eye should be in a state of relaxation, before the operator can check the static visual condition or the vision when the eyes are at rest of fixating at practical infinity, for our purpose - 20 feet away. This is the primary requirement when testing for best distance vision for everyday activity. The three principal methods, commonly used to determine the static state of the eye are

1. The Graphic method
2. The Physiological Exophoria method
3. The "Drops" cycloplegia or paralysis of the ciliary method.

The Graphic method is the one most commonly employed, and will serve well to demonstrate "What the Doctor is doing when he examines my eyes."

This method employs twenty-one different diagnostic steps so numbered to assist the Doctor in organizing and systemizing his work, so that he can correctly analyze the status of the eye. Most doctor's record charts allude to these points. Each point will be discussed separately.

The most common reasons a person seeks the service of a vision-care practitioner are: vision blurs, pain around the eyes, double vision, eye fatigue, eye tears, eyes usually red, ordinary lights bother the eyes, pain in the eye, dizziness, nausea, halos around lights, styes and headaches. For our purpose eye diseases are excluded, these all fall in one category.

1) The preliminary examination consists of inspection of the outward appearance of the eye. The doctor can readily detect what he would consider an abnormal external appearance. This could be redness, scaly, "bloodshot eyes," irregular eyelashes, or any inflammatory or sub-clinical process.

2) Here the ophthalmoscope is used. This usually is a hand-held light projecting instrument which contains a battery of lenses for the purpose of bringing into focus different areas of the interior of the eye. The instrument is held by the doctor approximately one inch from the patient's eye. You may hear several clicks which indicate a change in lens power required for the doctor to see the retinal area clearly. The iris, crystalline lens, optic nerve head, blood vessels and general eye grounds are examined with this instrument. Many diagnostic signs can be determined here: The existence of any general vascular abnormality such as hypertension (high blood pressure), kidney disorders or cerebral tumors, and also specific eye pathology such as detached retina, retinal hemmorhages, ballooning of retinal arteries (aneurysms), glaucoma (increase in intra-ocular pressure) inflammation of the iris (iritis), inflammation of the retina (retinitis) and many others. In fact, a very good idea of the general physical condition of the body can be thus determined. The interior of the eye is the only area of the body where the conditions of the blood vessels can be

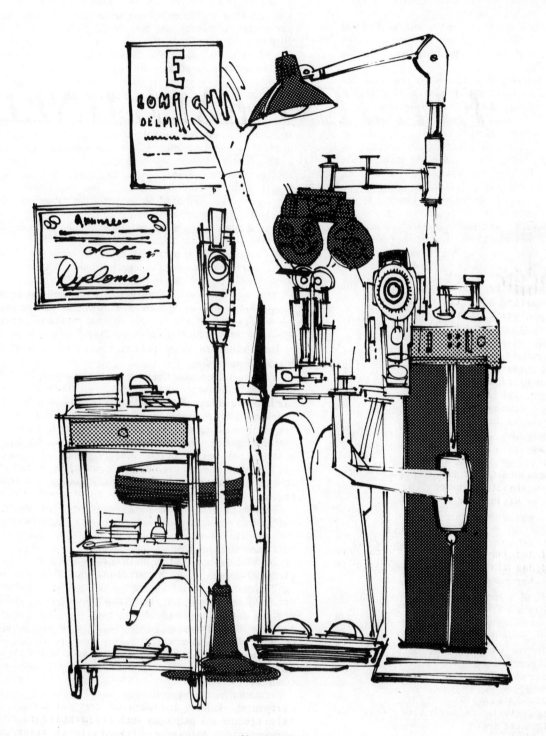

Hey Doc! I'm here.

seen and also photographed when necessary.

3) The ophthalmometer or keratometer is the large instrument which projects small lights onto the surface of the cornea (outer colored appearing surface of the eye). The chin-rest holds the head and eye in a steady and correct position. These lights are in the form of luminous mires* which can be measured. By examining and noting the position of these mires in two principal meridians, one ninety degrees away from the other, a determination can be made of the amount, type and position (axis) of any existing corneal astigmatism*. (Astigmatism* usually remains throughout one's entire life.)

This step is of great assistance in arriving at the final lens prescription. Several other lesser important factors are obtained, like any corneal irregularity due to trauma at some previous date.

4) At this point a determination is made of the muscular balance of the eyes in their natural state (without the aid of lenses). This is accomplished with rotary prisms which test the blurring, disassociation and focusing ability of the eye. A prism can cause doubling of vision, by rotating these prisms the doctor can ascertain the degree of normalcy of this function. The reason for making this test at this point is to be able to compare these findings with the results of the same test taken after a lens correction is obtained and to appraise the changes to the original muscle balance after the corrected lenses had been added. The doctors are familiar with the *zone of comfort*. This test will be an indication if the prescription will be worn with comfort. Slight variations can be made to adjust the prescription to be within the *zone of comfort*. (5 & 6). At this point a static refraction is performed. The instrument called the phoroptor which contains a battery of lenses and other ancillary testing equipment is adjusted before the eyes of the patient. The instrument is regulated to the anatomical pupillary distance which is determined by actual measurement from the right to the left pupil of the eye with a millimeter ruler. *The room is usually dark.* A light beam projected from a small hand-held instrument which resembles the ophthalmoscope, but is called a retinoscope, is directed to pass through the lenses of the phoroptor and enter the pupil of the eye. The doctor observes the reflex of this light by looking through a peep hole in this hand held instrument. The light is moved in all meridians. By rotating the lenses in the chamber in front of the eyes of the patient, the doctor can study the extent of the error of refraction or the lens discrepancy. Every type of basic refractive error can thus be determined. Technically an estimation of the conjugate* focus of the eye is here obtained. In this test the patient is asked to look at a distant point source of light, so that the point of fixation is about twenty feet. The same test is performed at thirteen or sixteen inches so that the near error can be noted. These are objective tests.

7) This next test is of a subjective nature. The patient offers his reaction to a refinement in the lens formula which was obtained previously. Here the ancillary lenses are put to work. Quite often the patient rejects the lenses obtained in the objective test, the previous test. Frequently nearsighted people subjectively accept stronger lenses, farsighted people weaker lenses than what their eyes require, according to the objective or instrument findings. The doctor must weigh these findings and arrive at a prescription which will offer the best comfortable vision for the intended purpose.

The balance of the tests are concerned with the near requirements for patients over 40 years of age or what is termed presbyopia* vision of the fifth decade of life.

8) The muscle-balance tests are performed with prisms after the determination of the distant and near prescription. This will give the doctor a very accurate concept

of the coordination of all eye functions.

Following the tests involving the effectiveness of lenses before the eye, a determination is made of the visual performance of the eye. This is called visual acuity and is measured by any variation of the Snellen Chart*: self-luminous, or one which is of the projector type, or just a plain cardboard eye chart. The formula representing the acuity may read 20/40. This means that the size Snellen letter which should be read clearly at forty feet, requires the patient to move to twenty feet to see clearly, a loss of 16.4% vision. 20/20 is normal. The most common rounded Snellen fractions used and their equivalent percentage of visual loss are 20/30 8.6%; 20/50 23.5%; 20/60 30.1%; 20/70 36.2%; 20/80 41.5%; 20/100 51.1%; 20/200 80%; 20/300 91.8%; 20/400 96.7%; 200/800 99.9%. The numerator is always the operating distance, the denominator refers to the smallest size letter the subject can read at the working or basic distance -- usually twenty feet.

It should be understood that there is no definitive correlation existing between the degree of focal deficiency of the eye and the Snellen scale. One individual requiring a lens correction of - 2.00 diopters* may see 20/200, another with the same dioptric deficiency of -2.00 has a visual acuity of 20/300 or 20/100. This may appear confusing, however, all eyes do not act alike. Other physical characteristics must be considered like color of the iris, size of the pupil, age of the patient and many physiological and psychological factors.

In California, as in most states, the Department of Public Social Services considers as legally blind 20/200 and therefore eligible for AB (aid to the blind). The degree of vision is that which cannot be corrected with regular glasses or contacts while using both eyes. Also eligible are those whose field of vision extends over a radius of only 10° from the center, constricted or tubular vision.

The California Motor Vehicle Bureau's most recent vision requirements for non - commercial drivers is a minimum of 20/67 for the worst eye, the field of vision to be 75° or better.

Flight hostesses (stewardesses) are required to have unaided vision in each eye of 20/30 or better. At present, the wearing of contact lenses is permitted in lieu of the stated requirements. However, vision without contacts must be at least 20/100 in each eye correctable to 20/30. Pilots are required to have unaided vision of 20/20 in each eye. These pre-employment qualifications are based on those for Continental Airlines.

Draftees for the Armed Services are given medical deferments when the dioptric* spherical equivalent of lens for one eye is greater than 8.00 plus or minus, or the corrected visual acuity is:

(1) 20/40 in one eye and 20/70 in the other eye.
(2) 20/30 in one eye and 20/100 in the other eye.
(3) 20/20 in one eye and 20/400 in the other eye.

or if any ordinary spectacles cause discomfort by reason of ghost images, prismatic displacement, or if consultation with an eye doctor reveals a condition which is disqualifying or any eye anomaly which impair the visual function requirement for satisfactory performance of military duty. The latter also includes a host of specific eye conditions.

The author is confident the foregoing factual explanatory offering of routine eye analysis will be appreciated for its simplification and informative material. There are numerous additional tests and measurements which can be made, including specialized tests for particular or rare infirmities, like the specific test for Glaucoma* in which an indentor is applied to the cornea in order to determine the intraocular pressure. However, as stated, these are included mainly when indicated. "Rare infirmities are rare."

L. MANASSE Co.,

MANUFACTURING OPTICIANS,

88 Madison St., CHICAGO.

Reduced price list for frames and lenses all other goods at proportionately low prices. Prescription work promptly executed. Catalogue on application.

Riding Bow Spectacles and Frames.

Per doz. without lenses.

No. 27 Alumnico Rd. frames				$2.40
" 27a	"	"	" cable temples	3.60
" 23 German Silver Rd. frames				1.80
" 34 Gold filled	"	"		5.50
" 34a	"	"	" " cable	7.20
" 34b	"	"	"	"
		warranted 10 years		7.50
" 34c	"	" Rd. frame, warranted 10 years, cable temple		9.00
" 54a Steel Nickle plated Rd. frames				1.80

Straight Temple Spectacles and Frames.
Per doz. without lenses.

No. 25 Alumnico Straight temple frames				$2.40
" 21 German Silver "	"	"		1.80
" 32 Gold filled	"	"	"	5.50
" 32a " "	"	"	"	
		warranted 10 years		7.50
" 43a Steel Nickle plated straight Tmp. frames				1.50

129 A & B.

129 D & E.

Per doz without lenses

129a Gold filled Eyeglass frames			4.50
129b " " " " warranted 10 yrs.			7.50
129d " " " "			4.50
129e " " " " warranted 10 yrs.			7.50

Interchangeable Lenses.
Per doz Pair

1st qual. perescopic Convex or c c Lenses
1 or o Eye polished edges 0.25 to 8 D 1.00
1st qual. Cement Bifocal lenses 1 or o Eye
0.25 to 8 D 3.75
1st " Perfection " " 1 or o Eye
0.25 to 8 D 4.50

HEADQUARTERS FOR
OPTICAL GOODS.

GOLD, GOLD FILLED, ALUMNICO SILVER, GERMAN SILVER AND STEEL SPECTACLE AND EYE-GLASS FRAMES.

American Standard Lenses
SPHERICAL, CYLINDRICAL .... AND COMPOUND ....

SEE OUR CATALOGUE PAGES 3 TO 43 FOR PRICES THAT WILL INTEREST YOU.

With the improved facilities and extended experience in our prescription department we are in a position to give our patrons the best of service in this line, each prescription carefully filled and examined and absolute accuracy guaranteed.

Prescription Books Sent Free on Application.

OTTO YOUNG & CO.

IMPORTERS AND JOBBERS

149--151 State Street,
CHICAGO, ILL

"JADE, THE JEWEL THAT GRANTS ALL DESIRES IN THIS WORLD

14

...AND THE NEXT"

This book has been produced primarily as a compendium devoted to a classification of American spectacles both antique and of the collectible category. The author has devoted more than three decades to their collection and data compilation. His memory is still fresh enough to recall the most insignificant modification or refinement of the structure and mechanics of the spectacle per se.

In all the years engaged in these activities, he has found that the Chinese have been particularly prolific and ornate in their creation of hand-wrought devices related to vision aids. The author feels that the reader should be apprised of a touch of the Orient.

Prior reference has been made with respect to the philosophical and sociological impact of the adornment of eyeglasses by certain strata of the Chinese aristocracy. A presentation will follow now, of the introduction of Jade into the realm of visual aids----the quizzer – the magnifier.

The Chinese, since antiquity, have been known to perform miracles with their delicate embroideries on shiny silks in striking colors and their exquisite bowls and vases of material named for their country--China--and its synonym, porcelain. The dainty carving in ivory and jade which contained symbolisms always related to long life, are renown throughout the universe. However, it is also known that China has stood still and kept to itself during the latter two thousand years of its lengthy existence.

Many of the finer examples of this ingenuity has shown up in a unique manner with respect to aids to vision. With-

in the last two centuries, the Chinese have recycled some of their artifacts and upgraded these to a present functional plateau. The jade embellishments and ornaments, part of the regalia of several centuries ago, have been salvaged and reused and exported for the curio markets of the world, mostly for the affluent American antique market.

The jade buckles (circa early nineteenth century) on the perishable mandarin robes have been removed and used as the handles for the ornate magnifiers (circa early twentieth century) illustrated as plate 46. The hand sculptured figures of the bat in Chinese symbolism is representative of "long life." Dragons – vigilance, the goodness and strength and the productive power of water. The floral arrangements are indicative of the months of the year and four seasons.

The cleverness exhibited by the Chinese in recycling the treasured carved jade of a previous century, thus producing a functional and saleable object d'art, is without equal in the annals of the history of antiques.

The hand-made petit point boutique ensemble (circa early nineteenth century) has as a part of its grouping an eyeglass case together with a change purse, fan holder and kerchief pocket. The Chinese symbols embroidered on each item translate to "Prolonged years good for long life." (See plate #1)

The February 1972 monumental meeting in China between President Nixon and Prime Minister Chou En-lai and Chairman Mao Tse-tung may result in changes which could alter its present economic structure.

156

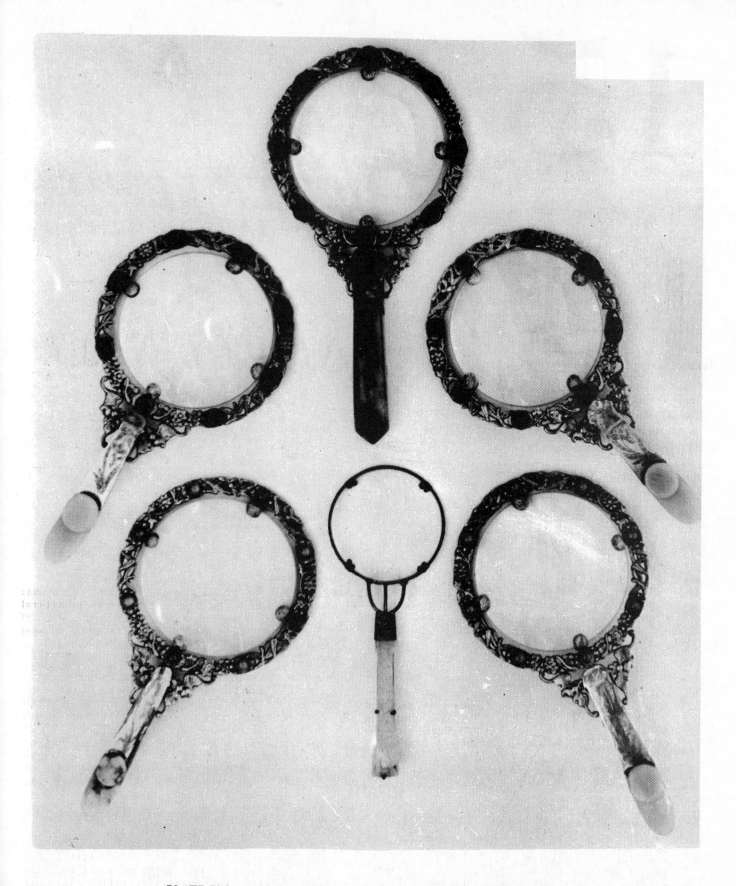

PLATE #46 *The fine outer ornate magnifiers are made with real jade C. 1820 and studded with jade rosettes or coral. Unusual and beautiful. Value of each $200.00. Constructed of gold plate over silver. Smaller central magnifier handle; white jade finely engraved; metal, silver C. 1800.*

157

15

BUYER BEWARE

Every writer on the subject matter concerned with the vast field of antiques and collectibles in general, invariably discusses and stresses the importance of being able to differentiate between the authentic specimen and the fake. Classic illustrations of gross fraud are voluminous.

A certain section of antique dealerships practice dating the origin of their wares and speak of centuries with the same unsubstantiated assurance as they do of decades. It is also evident that hypothetical eras of origin become factual when passed from dealer to dealer.

Historical sentimentalism often plays a prominent part in assessing a value to an antique spectacle, and may be the principal factor in creating buyer appeal.

Regarding the Chinese Quizzer photo plate 46 an antique dealer claimed it to be 400 years old. The trained eye will recognize this to be impossible. Particularly when he has observed that in this field of imports from foreign countries, especially China and Japan, much material enters with the country of origin affixed with a label, instead of stamped into the metal. This can be promptly removed. Even the required stamping has been known to be burnished out so as to be indiscernable. However,

in this instance the general appearance and the interesting piece of genuine jade may have caused the buyer to overlook its correct origin. The purchase could have been prompted mainly by intrigue. The buyer is often guilty of continuing the unorthodox practice of the dealer. The quizzer obviously is a recently manufactured import.

A further obvious inequity exists in the determination of the origin of spectacles as indicated by official correspondence dated February 16, 1972 and received by the author from the Smithsonian Institution in which a partial listing is given of the rare spectacle collecting in this national museum.

The following is a conformed list of the ones presenting a gross extant discrepancy and identified in plate #2: Spectacles, Chinese wooden rims (folding), held in place by silk cords, dated C. 600 A.D. "Spectacles, Chinese bronze frames, lens made of quartz, dated Ca. 800 A.D."

The writer offers his own interpretation after actually viewing similar models as items #2 and 4. The lenses in particular offer means for conjecture. (see spectacles held by Mr. Evers plate 47 and those portrayed in plate 43) The lenses are about .25 inch thick, round

PLATE 47

Maurice Evers prominent collector of long standing; has appeared on T.V., radio and mentioned in numerous newspaper and magazine articles.

and distinctly "plano" (without focus), and flat indicating polished plate glass. The purpose of such curios as mentioned previously was purely an affectation or a means of establishing a more elevated general rapport in society and especially at Court.

Caution must be exercised by the buyer with respect to possible confusion regarding the stamping practice. A 1/10 12K gold filled frame of high quality will even test like gold in a superficial acid test. Especially if the pads or bridge are marked 10K or 14K. This refers only to the parts so stamped, the balance may be gold filled or silver. Temples are interchangeable and may be solid gold while the front section is gold filled. This awareness refers only to "specs" circa Post Civil War. The better metals should command a higher price.

When a clamor is set in motion for certain rare objects, these become rarer and the price jumps proportionately. The exploiter's task is made easier, because the higher price level apparently is a greater inducement to the inexperienced collector. The amateur often judges quality by expensiveness and finds it difficult to distinguish the choice from the rare. The blatant charlatan is quick to take advantage of such opportunities *to make the deal.* This form of spurious merchandising has existed as far back as there has been sufficient demand and individuals who would risk the possible resulting legal penalties.

The author wishes to emphasize here that most dealers in antiques are sincere, honest and dedicated to their calling and if a seemingly fraudulent transaction occurs it is often unintentional. How many times has a Shakespeare "discovery" been accepted as authentic and later disclosed to be a forgery? History of collectibles abounds with such vignettes.

The author can only emphasize the urgency in his advice to prospective collectors of antique spectacles. "Get on the band wagon" despite the possibility of being "ripped off*."

In 1935, the Optical Manufacturer's Association, in accordance with the National Stamping Act, issued definite standards and specifications for the marking and stamping of optical frames and mountings made in whole or in part of gold. For example: Bausch & Lomb gold filled frame throughout is stamped B & L 1/10 12K GF. A gold filled center with a 10K solid gold bridge is stamped B & L 1/10 12K GF 7 for 14K gold bridge 9. The symbol 7 or 9 indicated that the part upon which the stamp appears only is 10K and 14K solid gold respectively.

Page 27 of the "American Optical Company" 1910 catalogue illustrates and explains their quality mark and trade marks. It is the oldest published information in their files. These indentifications would be helpful in the classification of a specimen. The follow:

TRADE MARKS

GOLD FILLED PATENTED STYLES

1–10	10 K	- - - - - -	©	↶	⊏
1–10	12 K	- - - - - -	©	↶	⊏◎
1–10	12 K with 1–5 12 K Bridge and Temple	- -	©	↶	⊡
1–10	14 K	- - - - - -	©	↶	E
1–8	14 K	- - - - - -	©	↶	⊓
1–10	12 K Bridge and Temple	-	©	↶	▽

SILVER

160 Coin Silver - - - - - - © COIN

GOLD

Quality			Mark
8 K	- - - - -	AOCo	✢
10 K	- - - - -	AOCo	⊖
14 K	- - - - -	AOCo	14K

GOLD FILLED

1–10	10 K	- - - - -	©	⊏
1–20	10 K	- - - - -	©	⊐
1–30	10 K	- - - - -	©	⊔
1–10	10 K Bridge and Temple	-	©	⊿

OTHER METALS

Quality			Mark
Steel	- - - -		Ⓢ
Alumnico	- - -		ALUMNICO
Alumnico (Pat. styles)	-		ALUMNICO PAT.
Alumnica	- - -		ALUMNICA
Regaloïd	- - - -		REGALOID
Roman Alloy	- - -		ROMAN ALLOY

MISCELLANEOUS

Trial Sets and Frames	-		AOCo
Lenses	- - - -		AOCo CENTEX
Spectacle Cases	- - -		©
Machinery	- - -		Ⓢ or AOCo
Ajax Strap	- - - -		Ⓐ
Imitation Leather	- -		VICAR
Black Enamel Finish	- -		JAPTOL
Readers	- - - -		AMOPTISCOPE

For Tagging Frames, Mountings, etc.

All manufacturers of metal frames are required to protect the consumer in this manner. The National Stamping Act provides that any firm that misrepresents the gold or silver content of a spectacle frame is guilty of a misdemeanor and may be punished by a fine of not more than $5,000.00 or imprisonment for not more than one year, or both. This stamping regulation applies equally to importers of metal frames which have been mismarked abroad or the markings altered after arrival.

As a result of the increase in the use of more gold for frames within the last decade, new regulations have been promulgated to update standards so as to meet present requirements. Hence, a revision of the 1935 regulation were effected on April 16, 1964.

This denunciation of standards should be helpful to the collector in identifying and appraising a specimen, and similarly promote fair dealing and public confidence in quality merchandise.

It has been brought to the attention of the author that within the past few years thoughts have been projected, especially by those who have been "ripped off*" and by organizations like the Better Business Bureau, concerning the advisability of state licenses to regulate antique dealers.

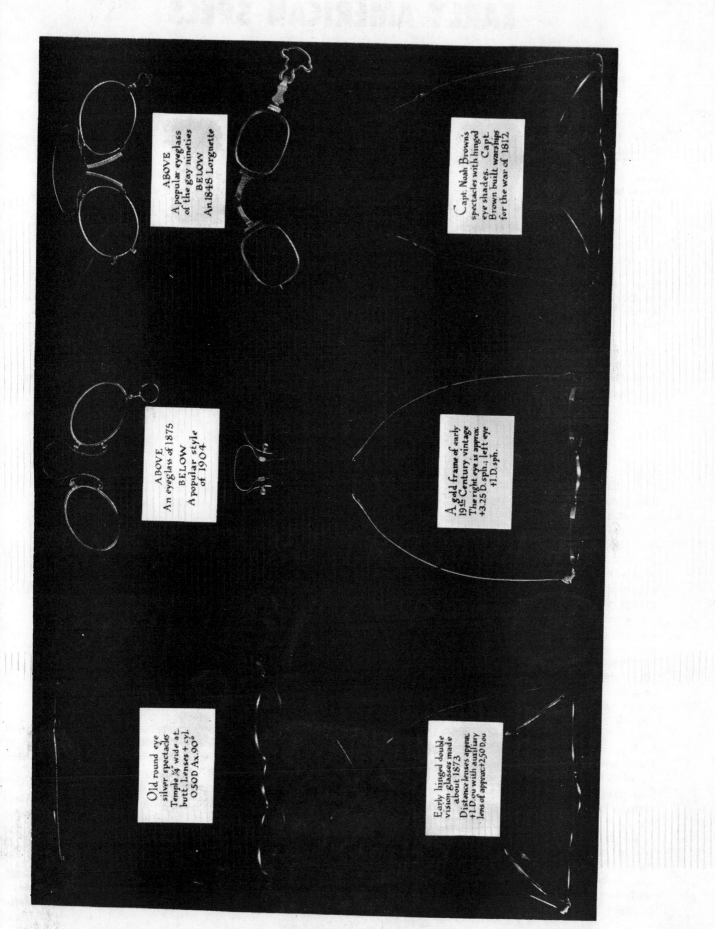

ABOVE
A popular eyeglass
of the gay nineties
BELOW
An 1848 Lorgnette

Capt. Noah Brown's
spectacles with hinged
eye shades. Capt.
Brown built warships
for the war of 1812

ABOVE
An eyeglass of 1875
BELOW
A popular style
of 1904

A gold frame of early
19th Century vintage.
The right eye is approx.
+3.25 D. sph., left eye
+1.D. sph.

Old round eye
silver spectacles
Temple ¼ wide at
butt. Lenses + cyl.
0.50 D Ax 90°

Early hinged double
vision glasses made
about 1873
Distance lenses approx.
+1.D. cu with auxiliary
lens of approx +2.50 cu

EARLY AMERICAN SPECS

AN EXCITING COLLECTIBLE.

by Dr. L. D. Bronson

Editor's Note: The author is a practicing optometrist in Sherman Oaks, California. His full length book "Early American Specs" is being published and is scheduled to be in the bookstores in the spring of 1973. He has written a great many articles related to the eyes and optical appliances including eyeglasses. He writes a column for the newspapers under the pseudonym of Dr. Eye. He is associate Editor of the 59 year old "Optometric World" which covers the fourteen western states including Texas, Alaska and Hawaii. This is read by vision-care specialists.

It is the considered opinion that his collection of eyeglasses and vision-care memorabilia is the largest and most outstanding in America, and is available to be seen by the public.

All photos are by **John Campbell** and are from the writer's private collection.

Plate No. 1

Plate No. 1 — Illustrates three of the earliest spectacles worn by the Colonists, circa 1620. These were mainly imports. The metal generally used was steel, silver or brass. The eye rims were all round in shape. The temples (sides/bows) fold on a turn-pin type swivel (earlier) (b), (c), or on a hinge arrangement (later) (a). The end loops of earliest circa were perfectly round and only a bit smaller than the eye rims. The earliest lenses prior to manufactured glass were fabricated from the natural mined forms and called beryl, pebble, (sections of quartz) or any clear rock formation like emerald and topaz. The distinction between the two can be appraised by the condensation factor. The native mineral will not steam up from the moisture of one's breath. The length-and-method of folding the temple serves as an additional indication of the age. Value $50-$100.

MRS. M, a lady of means, an avid collector of bric-a-brac, and a patient of mine, came to see me regarding her eyes. She had arrived at that age (presbyopia) when her hands were not long enough. Precisely, she needed glasses for near work (reading specs). The examination completed, she was escorted to the "frame bar" so that my assistant could help her select a suitable frame to house the corrective lenses. Without a moment's hesitation, she whipped out a beautifully engraved gold-filled lorgnette and implored that the prescribed lenses be ground to fit this greatly cherished memorabilia. No! It was not her great grandmother's. She had purchased this fine specimen from an antique dealer expressly to serve this utilitarian purpose. She had paid $65. for it . . . after some serious haggling . . . an excellent buy.

Several months later she came to see me again. This time with another silver colored lorgnette. She was now aware of my expertise with such antiques and hoped that I could tell her something about this new find, which she had purchased at an antique show while on vacation. She told me she had paid $7. plus $.35 tax, and the woman who sold it to her was concerned that she was asking too much. Mrs. M told me she thought it was broken since she had difficulty opening it. One look, and I knew it could not be silver (no patina). It was not of recent vintage, hence it could not be any of the modern metals (aluminum or magnesium).

Steel also has an easily identifiable lustre. I quickly sought the aid of my compound magnifier and, there it was, clear as day; beneath an accumulation of muck, I read, PLATINUM. Mrs. M had made a buy. The $7. purchase had a present value of $250. I also showed her the secret of how easily the lorgnette can be opened. (see illustration). I learned later that one of her affluent friends, Mrs. C, had seen her wearing the original gold-filled lorgnette

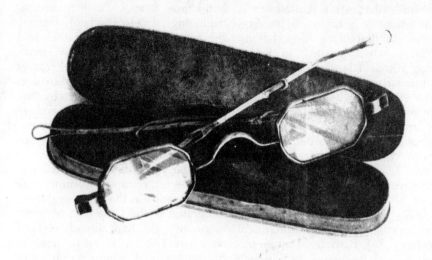

Plate No. 2 — Represents a refinement of those shown in Plate No. 1 by containing a number of improvements, to wit: refinement of shape; provision made for adjustment of the interpupillary. distance. The straights at both ends of the center bridge allow for some bending; the temple length can be regulated, (sliding). A reduction of thickness and improvement in quality of workmanship is also apparent. The steel case is well made, cloth-lined, and shows signs of greater versatility of the artisan. Circa late 18th century. Value $75.

Plate No. 2

Plate No. 3 — The beginning of the era of thin metal rims. Both finely constructed of solid gold. Lower left with turnpin temples. Upper right introduced the comfortable cabled temple. The purpose of the latter temples was to help keep the spectacles in place. The construction was spring-like. Many present-day frames are replicas of these, with only slight variations.

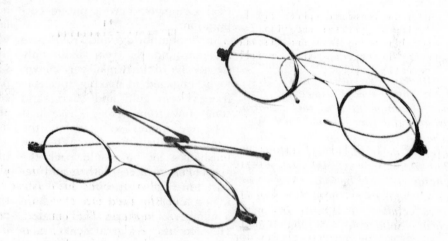

Plate No. 3

and asked that she be on the lookout for a similar one for her (the friend). Mrs. C intended it only as a charm. (no vision problem — an excellent conversation piece). Obviously, Mrs. M did not relinquish this find to her friend. As a result of this bonanza, Mrs. M is now an avid collector of antique specs, in addition to bric-a-brac.

There are more collectors of antique eyeglasses than can be imagined. In fact, there are now specialists within this vast area of collectibles. The writer is in constant touch with many of these, in particular a top-ranking film star, J.P., who specializes in collecting lorgnettes. These she has mounted in an illuminated shadowbox arrangement and will expound on their intriguing lore at the slightest provocation.

This vignette is fact not fiction and clearly demonstrates the paucity of information concerning knowledge of the value and the interest surrounding this exciting collectible. The writer can quote many such encounters.

Beginning with the era of the pilgrims (1620) and all during the days of our colonization, all spectacles were imported from the more industrialized countries like England, France, Germany and Italy. The first Colonist known to have worn eyeglasses was Peter Brown. At the time they were quite costly, as much as $200. It was only the literate and affluent who required the need for such a valuable and treasured appliance. Very few of the Pilgrims could spend so vast a sum or were able to read or write; furthermore, reading material of any kind was practically unavailable.

Foreign-made spectacles were the only ones in usage in this country for the next century. Those few made here were mostly hand-wrought and crudely made by artisans trained in metalcraft or jewelry work. George Washington's and Benjamin Franklin's eyeglasses have been preserved, in good condition, in their respective repository in Mount Vernon and Philadelphia.

At the turn of the nineteenth century, John McAllister of Philadelphia began manufacturing spectacles with sliding sides (temples) containing looped ends which afforded much easier manipulation with the then-popular wigs. The loop supplemented the inadequacy of stability by affording a means for the addition of a cord or ribbon which could be tied behind the head, thus holding the spectacles more firmly in place.

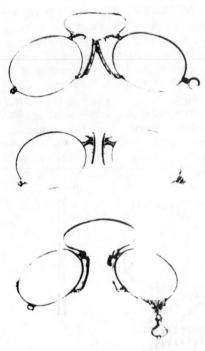

Plate No. 4

Plate No. 4 — The three specimens portrayed are called "pince nez", from the French. However, they were manufactured in this country around the time of the Civil War when importation of the original French make was practically nil. The bottom one is solid gold, hand-engraved, could be folded and worn on a chain as a charm. (Or was it an affectation, or symbol, or affluency?). Solid gold, $75. others, $35.

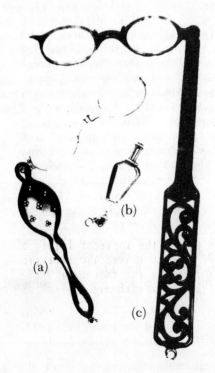

Plate No. 5 — (a) American-made folding lorgnette, circa 1900, set with seed pearls in sterling silver. Hand-held, when functional, or worn on a chain around the neck as an ornament. Fine craftsmanship. (b) Folding lorgnette charm-like construction, finely engraved, both useful and decorative, circa 1925. (c) Long-handled folding lorgnette made of genuine tortoise-shell, all hand-carved by a member of the writer's family, circa 1930. Value (a) $100, (b) $75, (c) Unique.

Plate No. 5

In 1826, William Beecher came to Southbridge, Massachusetts from Connecticut to establish a jewelry-optical manufacturing shop, having served as an apprentice in Providence, Rhode Island. The first ophthalmic articles he produced were silver spectacles which were later followed by blue steel. In 1869, the American Optical Company was incorporated and absorbed the holdings of William Beecher, et al. The debut of a lens grinding plant in 1883 precluded the need for importation of lenses from France and Germany. Sixteen years prior to the incorporation of American Optical Company, J. J. Bausch set up an optical shop in Rochester, N.Y. which has since evolved into one of the foremost optical establishments in the world, the Bausch & Lomb Optical Company, now a public corporation.

In the Southbridge and Providence area, around the year 1830, only twenty-five or thirty men were known to be engaged in making spectacle frames from gold and silver, and some few from steel. Those first spectacle frames were mainly the work of William Beecher. When he finished a lot he would pack the spectacles in his carpetbag and depart for Boston, specifically Washington and Bromfield Streets, where a number of opticians had located. He encountered a great deal of sales resistance in his efforts to sell these handmade frames. Prior to his introducing American-made frames, the imported spectacle frames had cost less. With difficulty he managed to sell four dozen steel frames before returning to Southbridge. From this apparently sketchy beginning evolved the vast empire of the American Optical Corporation — the largest producers of optical appliances in the world.

Similarly, in 1849 J. J. Bausch, the founder of a most impressive optical empire at the age of eighteen, emigrated to the United States from Germany. He had already served an apprenticeship as an optician in his native land where gainful employment in this specialized occupation was extremely scarce. Prior to his coming to the United States he found work in Berne, Switzerland for an optical establishment where spectacles were made from the basic raw material. His compensation for the labor on a complete pair of spectacles was equal to six cents. By working hard at it, he was able to complete six pairs of spectacles per day. All work was manual or by foot power. Steam or electricity to operate the machinery was still in its infancy.

Mr. Bausch encountered difficult times in America from 1849 until prior to 1861 and the advent of the Civil War. During that interim Mr. Bausch, who possessed an ingenious experimental aptitude, developed a method of making spectacle rims from hard rubber, which proved to be particularly adaptable for the intended purpose. Previously, working horn (from animals) proved unsatisfactory because of its brittle characteristic. In the spring of 1861, when war broke out, only few spectacles frames could be imported, hence, the demand for the rubber frame zoomed. Continuous expansion followed. The facilities at the enlarged plant allowed for numerous improvements and diversification. In addition to spectacle lenses and frames, other optical devices were initiated into the production schedule. Binoculars, microscopes, optical devices for the precision requirements of the flourishing moving picture industry, and a multitude of related instruments were added to the rostrum. The original name of Vulcanite

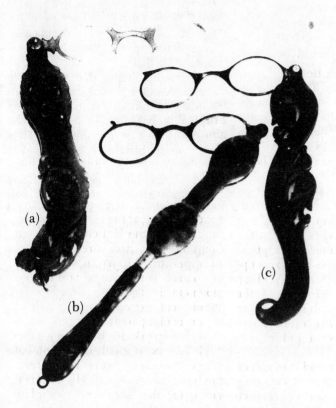

Plate No. 5a

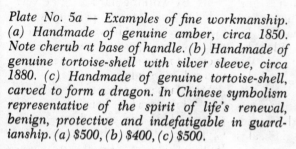

Plate No. 6

Plate No. 5a — Examples of fine workmanship. (a) Handmade of genuine amber, circa 1850. Note cherub at base of handle. (b) Handmade of genuine tortoise-shell with silver sleeve, circa 1880. (c) Handmade of genuine tortoise-shell, carved to form a dragon. In Chinese symbolism representative of the spirit of life's renewal, benign, protective and indefatigable in guardianship. (a) $500, (b) $400, (c) $500.

Plate No. 6 — Four specimens of folding lorgnettes which are the most sought after. All precious metal of high quality (the oval one is 22kt., circa 18th century, French). The octagonal is platinum, including the slide, and is valued at $500. It is still functional, all hand-engraved, circa 1920. The lorgnette with the longer handle, circa 1900, is opened with the same special catch as that of Mrs. M's platinum lorgnette. The three-rings at the base of the handle slides two ways for releasing the catch. This method of closure is found only in the finer specimens. The smaller handled lorgnette is embellished with enamelling. Oval $250, Octagon $500, Long-handle $350, Shorter-handle $250.

Optical Instrument Company was changed to Bausch and Lomb Company. In 1911, this company employed over 2000 people. Today, prior to automation, the roll was 10,000. After the institution of computers and such, notwithstanding additional diversification like the "Soflens", the total remaining is 5,000.

Other present-day large producers of optical frames had their inception early in the nineteenth century. Many were gobbled up lately and merged to form conglomerates. When they first began, their basic product — spectacle frames and lenses — was exceptionally well made by fine artisans. The spectacle frames produced at that time are worth the high consideration of today's collector.

At first, frames were produced primarily to satisfy the requirement of being functional . . . ovals, round,

and rectangular. Later, the need for styling pervaded the consumers' appeal.

The demands of the style-conscious wearer brought about continuous changes in an effort to create a satisfactory rapport; a heavyweight plastic frame for the bold, in which the glasses were expressly designed to be so obviously an encumbrance as to portray a dis-

oriented, inharmonious appendage. The more extreme the spectacle, the greater the apparent display of individuality or else, an inconspicuous, rimless and thin metal frame for those who preferred frames supposedly to blend with their facial characteristics . . . their cosmetic appearance.

A prospective collector of antique eyeglasses will observe from the

165

photographs that it takes no substantial amount to start or continue a collection. Exciting specimens can still be found by the diligent buyer. However, caution should be exercised when purchasing a specimen over $25. The present market offers near replicas of recent manufacture. These are also artificially antiqued by a process of electroplating and etching. The principal purpose is not one of fraudulence but that the demand is great for simulated antique spectacle frames, which are in short supply.

About 1966, the advent of the "hippy" group included a rebirth to the wearing of spectacles of vintage between 1850 to 1930. This movement appeared to emanate as part of their tenets; their desire to identify with those "good ole days". This gave great impetus to the demand for so-called "groovy eyeglasses" interpreted in the form of "wires" circa 1920-1940.

The writer hopes that this article may serve as a stimulus to those already consumed with collecting "specs" and to others who may be inspired to start a collection. They will undoubtedly become aware of the tremendous sociological impact "specs" have made upon Early American History and maybe collectors will organize and correspond and learn from one another. Perhaps Teddy Roosevelt's pince nez will be unearthed . . . The writer would offer a "bundle" for these.

National Antiques Review

Reproduction of an old etching showing itinerant spectacle vending.

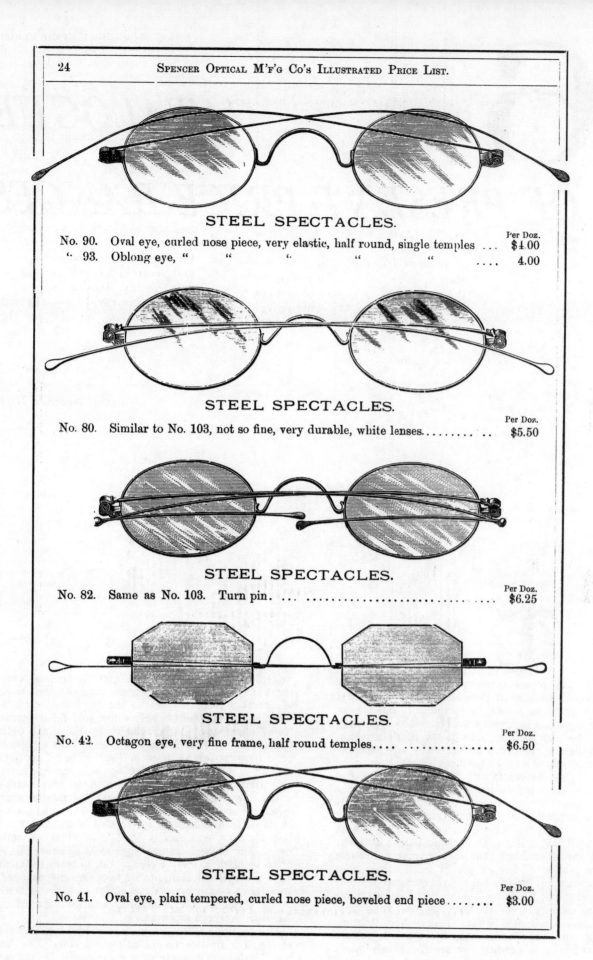

STEEL SPECTACLES.

Per Doz.

No. 90.   Oval eye, curled nose piece, very elastic, half round, single temples ... $4.00

" 93.   Oblong eye, "   "   "   "   " 4.00

STEEL SPECTACLES.

Per Doz.

No. 80.   Similar to No. 103, not so fine, very durable, white lenses......... .. $5.50

STEEL SPECTACLES.

Per Doz.

No. 82.   Same as No. 103.   Turn pin. $6.25

STEEL SPECTACLES.

Per Doz.

No. 42.   Octagon eye, very fine frame, half round temples.... .... $6.50

STEEL SPECTACLES.

Per Doz.

No. 41.   Oval eye, plain tempered, curled nose piece, beveled end piece........ $3.00

167

16

CATALOGUE

OF PRESENT PRICE RANGES

he following explanatory notes apply generally to all spectacles of which the antique trader must avail himself in order to make a purchase where the price paid may be realistic. It may bolster one's ego to make a buy, where the intrinsic and monetary value of the specimen far exceeds the purchase price. However, the real purpose is not served by such handling. Purchases should be made with only one purpose in mind. . . that it satisfies the buyers esthetic requirements or that it serves a proposed utilitarian need. Slight variation in price should not be questioned. Very old and poorly preserved spectacles may require restoration. The buyer must be able to distinguish those which will lend themselves to such additional mechanical implementation. Basically all parts should be intact. The screws, pins and dowels should be workable. Lenses are of small consequence unless very old and the original natural elements.

The prices quoted relate to the retail asking price samplings obtained from shoppers in New York City; Boston, Massachusetts; Dallas, Texas; New Orleans, Louisiana; and Los Angeles, San Diego and San Francisco, California. In addition, the benefit of the author's 30 years experience in collecting is included.

The buyer should avoid confusion by understanding that at the moment of manufacture several selling prices existed which were contingent with the trading level of the buyer. The price range was dependent on the area of operation with respect to the final consumer. For example, in 1925 an Olympic white gold filled engraved frame (See Adv.) manufactured by Universal Optical Corporation of Providence was offered to the "jobber*" or distributor at $3.50 each. The "jobber," the intermediary, sold to the retailer who was the optometrist, ophthalmologist or dispensing optician at a mark-up which was usually 40% above cost. The retailer therefore paid about $5.00 for the frame. The usual mark-up by the dispenser, any of the three O's mentioned in the last sentence, was usually 300% to about $15.00 selling price. The present antique buyer must be aware that this price includes a service charge which covers the attendant's professional ability to aid in cosmetic appeal and to take facial measurements and advise as to the suitability of the frame for the intended application, in addition to the usual overhead expenses.

The condition of the spectacle is divided into four categories. The first three are self-explanatory. The "used poor" refers to a specimen which is repairable but parts missing or requiring considerable restorative work. Prices include lenses and frames individually or glazed.

169

GENERAL PRICE RANGE

Classification Circa	Composition Material	New Gem	Condition Used Fine	Used Good	Used Poor
Pre-Revolutionary 1620-1774*	Steel	(unique) $500 to $2000	200.00	100.00	25.00
Revolutionary 1775-1811	Bronze, Brass, Steel	100.00	50.00	25.00	12.50
	Silver	125.00	65.00	35.00	15.00
	Gold 10, 14, 18 kt	150.00	100.00	50.00	35.00
War of 1812 1812-1845	Bronze, Brass, Steel	50.00	35.00	25.00	10.00
	Silver	65.00	50.00	30.00	20.00
	(Thin) Gold 10, 14, 18 kt	100.00	65.00	35.00	25.00
Mexican War 1846-1861	Bronze, Brass, Steel	35.00	25.00	15.00	10.00
	Silver	50.00	35.00	25.00	15.00
	Gold 10, 14, 18 kt	100.00	65.00	35.00	25.00
	Eye Glass Hard Rubber	25.00	15.00	10.00	7.50

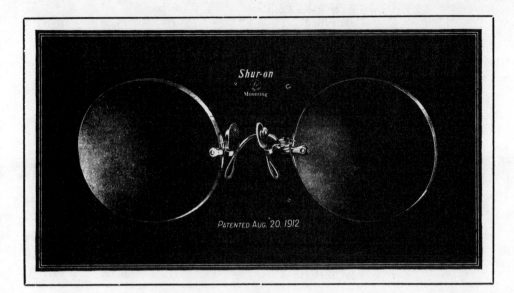

Civil War 1861-1868	Steel, Nickel	25.00	15.00	10.00	5.00
	Silver	35.00	20.00	15.00	10.00
	Gold 10, 14, 18 kt	75.00	50.00	30.00	20.00
	Eye Glass Hard Rubber	25.00	15.00	10.00	7.50
	Eye Glass Gold, Gold Filled	25.00	15.00	10.00	7.50
	Finger Piece Gold, Gold Filled	25.00	15.00	10.00	7.50
Indian Wars 1869-1897	Alumnico, Nickel	15.00	12.50	10.00	5.50
	(Thin) Gold 10, 14, 18 kt	50.00	35.00	25.00	20.00
	(Thin) Gold Filled or Plated	15.00	10.00	7.50	5.00
Spanish-American 1898-1913	Alumnico 0,00,000**	15.00	10.00	7.50	5.00
	Gold Filled	15.00	10.00	7.50	5.00
	All Types Pince Nez Gold 10, 14, 18 kt	25.00	15.00	10.00	5.00
	Gold Filled	15.00	12.50	7.50	3.50
World War I 1914-1921	Finger Piece with Reels and Hairpin Chains	15.00	12.50	7.50	3.50
	Oxfords GF Silver	75.00	50.00	15.00	10.00
	Oxfords Solid Gold	100.00	75.00	50.00	35.00
	0-00-000 Frames GF	10.00	8.50	6.50	3.00
	Real Tortoise	50.00	40.00	30.00	20.00
Pre-World War II 1922-1938	Fits U	12.50	10.00	7.50	3.00
	Windsor Frames	15.00	10.00	5.00	2.50
	Round Eye Alumnico	12.00	8.00	4.00	2.00
	Round Eye GF	15.00	10.00	5.00	3.50
	Zylonite	10.00	5.00	---	---
	Medium Weight Solid Gold Round	75.00	50.00	35.00	25.00
	Gold Filled Paded	15.00	10.00	5.00	3.50
	Ful Vue GF	15.00	10.00	5.00	3.50
	Rimless GF	15.00	10.00	5.00	3.50
	Rimless Solid Gold 10, 14 Kt	40.00	30.00	20.00	15.00
	Semi-Rimless	10.00	8.00	5.00	2.50
	Wils Edge	10.00	8.00	5.00	2.50
	Numont-Rimway	20.00	15.00	10.00	5.00
World War II 1939-1950	(Metal Restricted) GI Only	15.00	10.00	7.50	4.00
	Zylonite	2.00	1.00	---	---
Korean 1950-1953	Zylonite	2.00	1.00	---	---
	Air Corps Metal Goggle	10.00	7.50	3.00	---

Vietnamese
1962-1973

Rebirth of use of metal, rimless and goggles (see above for prices). Antiques and collectibles which can be refurbished. Note: For prices of Lorgnettes, Oxfords, and novelty visual appliances, see price referring to illustrated plates.

Price of gold frames quoted prior to the gold trajectory of 1973. . .Add 200% to approximate present quotes.

* Dates represent circa of popularity of specimen only.
** 0,00,000 refers to a method of measurement of the eye size of a thin metal oval frame.

Courtesy Bausch and Lomb: Collection from 1753 to the present (1955). Rimless having rebirth at present.

PRESENT PRICE RANGE
OF ILLUSTRATED SPECIMENS

Description	Price Range (Retail)
Benjamin Franklins and Case	$ 200.00 - $ 300.00
Looped Straight Temples Blue Steel Frame and Case	30.00 - 75.00
Adjustable Temples Case and Frame Silver	100.00 - 200.00
Pre-Revolutionary Steel (1738)	100.00 - 200.00
Revolutionary A. or B.	100.00 - 200.00
Pre-Civil War Solid Gold	100.00 - 200.00
Civil War Silver, Bronze	75.00 - 150.00
Civil War Solid Gold	125.00 - 250.00
Pre-World War I Steel - Alumnico	15.00 - 25.00
Pre-World War I Solid Gold	75.00 - 150.00
Pre-World War I Grab Fronts - Alumnico	15.00 - 20.00
Lorgnette Wishbone - Silver	250.00 - 500.00
Lorgnette Silver - Tortoise Case	200.00 - 300.00
Lorgnette Handmade 1850 Filigree	200.00 - 450.00
Lorgnette 1856 - Duchess of Luxenberg	500.00 - 1000.00
Lorgnette 1850 - Long Handle Silver Ring	200.00 - 400.00
Lorgnette Platinum (1920)	500.00 - 1000.00
Lorgnette 18 kt Solid Gold (1900)	250.00 - 500.00
Lorgnette 18 kt Solid Gold (1920)	300.00 - 500.00
Lorgnette Spencer Optical Company	150.00 - 250.00
Lorgnette Folding Short Handle	150.00 - 250.00
Lorgnette Diamond Studded Inlaid (1930)	1000.00 - 2000.00
Lorgnette All Tortoise (1830)	250.00 - 400.00
Pince Nez Hard Rubber	35.00 - 75.00
Hoop Spring Circa 1910 W.G.F.	25.00 - 60.00
Hoop Spring Circa 1910 Solid Gold	75.00 - 100.00
Hoop Spring Tortoise Circa 1925 G.F. Spring	20.00 - 30.00
Straight Spring Eye Glass Solid Gold 1900	75.00 - 100.00
Straight Spring Eye Glass G.F. and Case	50.00 - 75.00
Straight Spring Eye Glass Rimless	35.00 - 75.00
Hoop Spring All Steel	25.00 - 40.00
Hoop Spring and Stabilizer (1825)	75.00 - 100.00
Folding Oxford White Gold (Circa 1925)	125.00 - 175.00
Oxford Non-Folding White Gold (Circa 1925)	75.00 - 100.00
Oxford Folding Shell and Metal (1925)	50.00 - 75.00
Quizzer 1780 (Oval)	150.00 - 200.00
Quizzer Round	150.00 - 200.00
Quizzer (Circa 1910)	15.00 - 25.00
Goggle Motorcycle (1915)	25.00 - 50.00
Sunglasses 19th Century	25.00 - 50.00
Motor Glass 18th Century	100.00 - 150.00
Motor Glass 19th Century	50.00 - 75.00
Groovy Glasses	15.00 - 25.00
George Washington Glasses	Unique
Magnifiers Large Jade	150.00 - 200.00
Magnifiers Smaller	100.00 - 150.00
Magnifiers Smallest	100.00 - 150.00

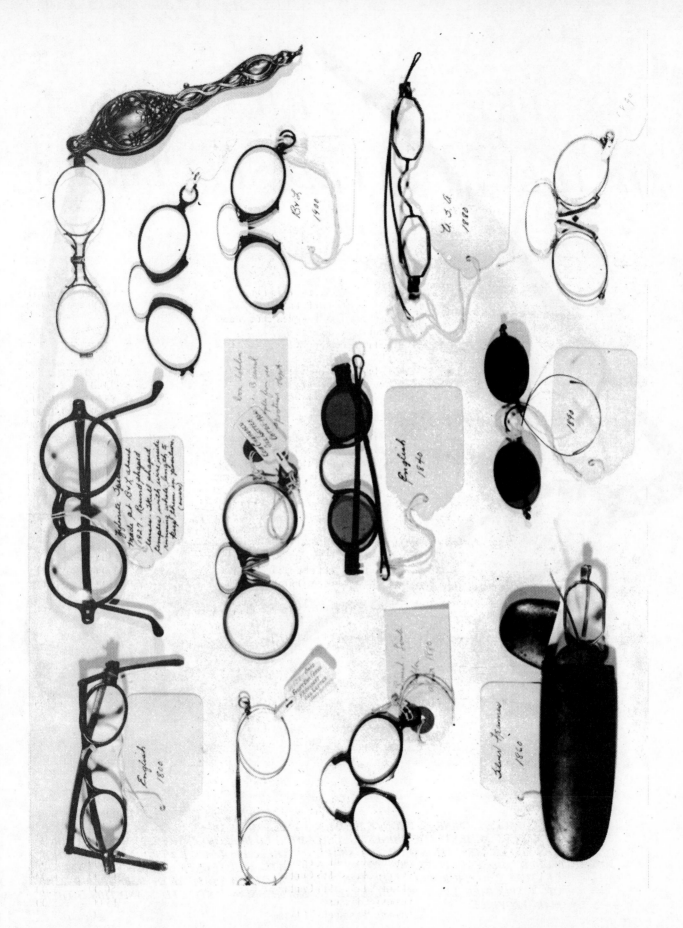

Courtesy Bausch and Lomb: Collection of assorted specs C. 1800–1927.

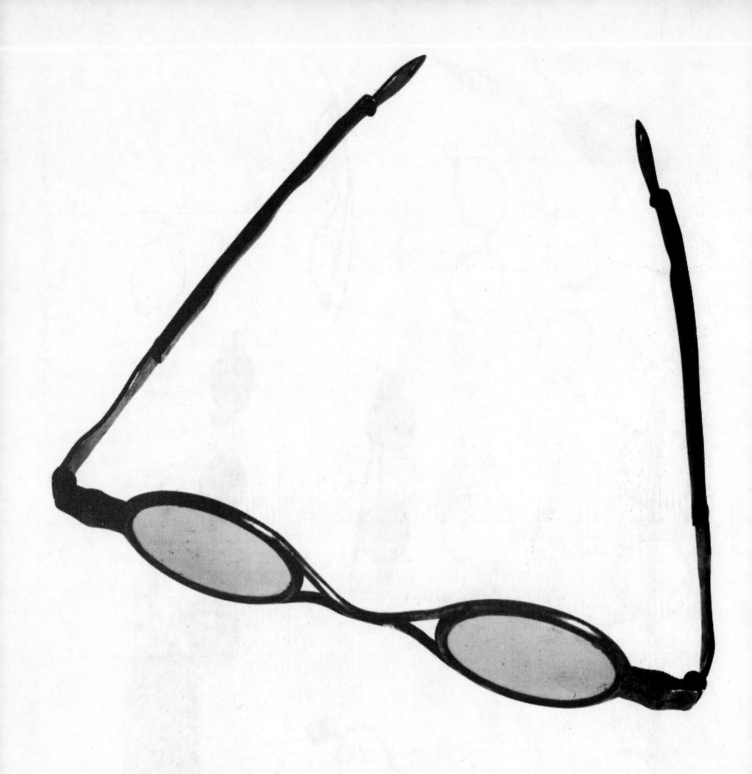

"SPECTACLES, CHINESE, BRONZE FRAMES, LENSES MADE OF QUARTZ, DATED CA. 800 A.D. AUTHOR'S COMMENT: THE CHINESE SELDOM WORKED IN BRONZE. THEIR METAL OF CHOICE WAS SILVER. TRADITIONALLY THE SHAPE OF THEIR PRODUCT WAS ROUND. THE AUTHOR WOULD JUDGE THIS FRAME TO BE CIRCA LATE EIGHTEENTH OR EARLY NINETEENTH CENTURY AND PROBABLY MADE IN GERMANY. ANOTHER EXAMPLE OF IMPROPER DATING OF A SPECIMEN EVEN BY THE EXALTED SMITHSONIAN INSTITUTE. . .AND THIS IS THEIR MAIN PROVINCE.

17 GLOSSARY

A. O. Common abbreviation for American Optical Corporation.

A. R. P. Refers to Argyll Robertson Pupil. The pupil is distended and will not contract to a strong light stimulus. A fixed pupil. This condition usually indicates syphilis of the central nervous system. Syn. Vincent's sign.

Adnexa All areas immediately surrounding the eye itself, like the lids, lashes and folded skin.

Amber A yellow or brownish-yellow translucent pine tree sap and fossil resin found in Alluvial soils and on some seashores. It is hard, easily polished and quickly electrified by rubbing. Russia is considered the Amber capital of the world. Elektron is the Greek word for Amber and the word electricity comes from it.

Antiqued Stemming from the continued requests made by patients in his practice for antiques or antique appearing spectacles, the author has developed a process of antiquing metal frames. The process consists of a penlight battery powered brushed on electroplating solutions in a variety of formulae consistent with the requirements for color. His information was obtained from a book published in England, called *Metal Coloring* published by Robert Draper, Ltd. Of course a formal rectifier and assorted plating electrolites and anodes would serve to a greater advantage. See reprint of article on antiquing.

Anti-Static Test When a piece of genuine tortoise shell is rubbed against another substance, static electricity is generated enough to lift a small piece of paper.

Astigmatism A difference in the radius of curvature of two principle meridians which are 90 deg. apart creating a blurred retinal image. The focus is a line (Sturms interval) rather than a point.

Bausch, J. J. In 1849 J. J. Bausch the founder of a most impressive optical empire emigrated at the age of eighteen to the United States from Germany. He had already served an apprenticeship as an optician in his native land where gainful employment in this specialized occupation was extremely scarce. Prior to his coming to the United States he found work in Berne, Switzerland for an optical establishment where spectacles were made from the basic raw material. His compensation for the labor on a complete pair of spectacles was equal to six cents. By working hard at it, he was able to complete six pairs of spectacles per day. All work was manual or by foot power. Steam or electricity to operate the machinery was still in its infancy. Mr. Bausch encountered difficult times in America from 1849 until prior to 1861 and the advent of the Civil War. During that interim Mr. Bausch, who possessed an ingenious experimental aptitude, developed a method of making spectacle rims from hard rubber, which proved to be particularly adaptable to spectacle frame rims. Previously, working American horn proved unsatisfactory because of its brittle characteristic. In the spring of 1861, when war broke out few optical appliances could be imported, hence, the demand for the rubber frame zoomed. A situation of continuous expansion became apparent. The facilities at the expanded plant allowed for numerous improvements and diversification. In addition to spectacle lenses and frames other optical devices were initiated into the production schedule. Binoculars, microscopes, optical devices for the precision requirements of the flourishing moving picture industry, and a multitude of related instruments were added to the rostrum. The original name of Vulcanite Optical Instrument Company was changed to Bausch & Lomb Optical Company. In 1911 this company employed over 2,000 people. Today, prior to automation the roll was 10,000. After the institution of computers and such, notwithstanding additional diversification like the "Soflens*" the total remaining is 5,500.

Benjamin Franklin

1706-1790. He was credited with the invention of bifocals. A bifocal is a lens having approximately a horizontal dividing line. The focus of the upper portion intended to correct the distant vision, the lower portion for the close or near vision. His invention consisted of two separate lenses held together by the outer rim of the spectacle. Many improvements have been made as a result of modern technology whereby two foci have been ground from one piece of glass to form a bifocal. Two pieces of glass of different index of refraction fused together and ground to the curve will result in a bifocal. Glass heated and dropped into a variety of forms to obtain a variance in focal power will also result in two foci. The most recent adaptation is where a dual focus is obtained by the moulding of transparent plastics to different lens curvatures hence, resulting in different foci. In 1783 two years prior to Franklin's description of the split bifocal, Addison Smith an Englishman, invented double spectacles. The distant correction was mounted in a metal spectacle with a special hinge arrangement whereby the near also mounted in a metal frame can be superimposed on the distant. This type of double spectacle is still available and serves a specialized application for surgeons, dentists or artisans whose requirements are of exacting measures and where segmented lenses are not as effective for near application. Thomas Jefferson also designed a bifocal in 1806. In appearance and in operation it resembled that of Benjamin Franklin's.

Black Panthers

A national organization mainly of blacks, dedicated to revolutionary ideals relative to assimilation of black power, lately non-violent and political.

Blue Jeans

The author wishes to comment on the extent of desecration to which a pair of new blue jeans are subjected before they are approved as the correct tenure for attire. Discoloration, patches and tears only improve their station. It is also interesting to note that at this writing "Head*" shops in London send scouts or buyers to the backwood areas of the U.S. to seek out as many as available that are still in one piece. . .authentic blue jeans worn by the farm and working class. These are shipped to London where the "Head" shops easily dispose of these at a premium. "The buyers want the real thing!"

Bows

See temples.

Bread

Funds. Money required in trading.

Bull, Dr. W. C.

Optometrist, earliest of American antique spectacle collectors aided with his collection in developing History of Eyeglasses and Spectacles for American Encyclopedia of Ophthalmology. (1915)

Cardiologist

Medical specialist in disorders of the heart.

Circa

Around the date (give or take a decade)

Columbia Resin 39	This refers to a transparent monomer of the thermo setting class which is greatly used in most commercial plastic ophthalmic lenses.
Compound lenses	A combination of spherical and cylindrical lenses which corrected both nearsightedness or farsightedness (spherical) and astigmatism (cylinder) in one lens. The astigmatism on the convex side the spherical element on the concave side. Newer computations have reversed this placement of elements. The reason given is that this newer method minimizes distortions and makes for greater wearing comfort.
Conjugate focus	Refers to two points in an optical system such that the rays originating at one are focused at the other and vice versa.
Dig this	This is to my liking.
Diopter	A means of measuring the focal power of an ophthalmic lens. (D-1/F) Diopters equals the reciprocal of the focal point.
Donders (Donder's table)	Wrote the classic work in 1864 "Refraction and accommodation of the eye". His work included a table of lag of accommodation and its relationship to age. An important work called Donder's Table of Expecteds.
Ecchymosis	Discoloration of the eye due to trauma. "Black eye".
Findings	In the optical industry this term applies to the small parts manufactured by specialists. The gold eyewire already grooved is manufactured by a gold fabricating shop. The screws and rivets and hinges by another, the rocking pearltex or plastic pads still another, and so on. These parts are made to the specifications of the ultimate assembler of the complete frame. The manufacturer also sells to the jobber, laboratory, or direct to the vendor or dispenser.
Finger Piece Mounting	Same as "Fits U." Contains a solid bridge with two pads on each side which press on each side of the nose. Tension to these pads are supplied by very small coil springs.
Fitover	Thin metal or zylonite rims attached by a flat spring containing sun lenses. This can "fit over" the regular spectacle glasses. The fit over frame can be used also with the near additions; grab front, see page.
Flea Market	An area where people gather to barter commodities not unlike a swap meet. The names are interchangeable. The same activity in one area can be called by one name, in another by the other name.
Ful Vue	A frame where the temple portion is elevated to the uppermost portion of the eyerim.
Funky	A latter outgrowth and the equivalent of "groovy."
Fuzz	Police or other formal authoritative groups.
Glass	Glass is composed of a mixture of silicates of the earth or heavy metals, as follows: (1) Flint pebbles or siliceous sand. (2) Sodium or potassium as carbonates or sulfates. (3) Limestone or marble. These are pulverized, mixed and heated to a point where the components are fused together. Thereafter it is subjected to a precalculated cooling process and polished. About 1945 glass was supplemented by a practical transparent Thermosetting plastic CR 39. Prior to that a Methyl Methacrylate, also a plastic but of poorer adaptability, was employed.
Glaucoma	An eye condition of increased intraocular pressure.
Groovy	In a pleasant manner.

Groovy Eyeglasses	Refers to thin metal rimmed glasses also rimless and Air Corps goggles. Wires.
Gullstrand	Standardized precise measurements of the schematic eye. Introduced Slit Lamp in 1911 which is indispensable in contact lens work. Presents highly magnified view of anterior section of eye and adnexa. Considerable credence was extended to scientific research relevant to the function of the eye, when in 1911 the Nobel Prize in physiology and medicine was awarded to Allvar Gullstrand whose research disclosed an explanation of the workings of the focusing apparatus of the eye. His discovery laid claim to the principle that accommodation of the eye is accomplished mainly by a rearrangement of its internal parts and only to a degree by changes in the retina. It has since been shown that this is not altogether true. However, this was the beginning.
Gutenberg's Development	Robert Jordan, a librarian, wrote in Strechert - Hafner Book News, 1967, "It's clear to us that eyeglasses are of basic importance to our way of life. What a different country we would live in if half or more of our population could not read books, newspapers or correspondence or, in most cases could not earn a living in almost any profession. Most of our great men now living would be helpless without eyeglasses."
Gutta Percha	A rubber-like substance formed by the milky juice of certain trees in Malaysia. It does not break easily and can be stretched when heated.
Half Eyes	Sometimes referred to as Ben Franklin's (a misconception) consists of the bottom portion of the spectacle arranged so that the wearer can look over the top of these. They are used always for close work such as reading, sewing, etc. Individuals who have normal distant vision but require glasses for near, find these convenient.
Hall of Presidents	Is an attraction which consists of life sized wax figures of all the U.S. Presidents to date attired in the customary fashion. This includes authentic replicas of all accouterments even to their spectacles: eight pair of these were supplied by the author.
Hallmarks	Stamping or marking of identification on precious metals including spectacle frames. In England served as an indication of payment of manufacturers tax.
Harlequin	A design and patented frame in which the shape of the eyewire simulated that of an ellipse with the temple attached to one end of the ellipse. The shape was placed on the diagonal to emulate the appearance of an harlequin mannequin.
Helmholtz	Herman Von Helmholtz (1851) invented the ophthalmoscope. The entire fundus of the eye (background) can be seen by the operator. The fundus is the only part of the body where blood vessels can be viewed and studied. It is of greatest value in cardiology, neurology, ophthalmology, optometry and as a diagnostic tool for any reno-vascular study.
Hip Generation	Those who follow what their mind dictates: Individualists
Hyperopia	Farsightedness, incident parallel rays entering the eye come to a focus behind the retina. The term is a misnomer, when expressed in this popular definition: "Can see far and not near". The fault lies in that some afflicted with Hyperopia in a degree high enough where vision is poor both for distance and near.
Impact Resistant	All lenses must be submitted to a test in accordance with standards set up by the FDA whereby the lens must be able to resist the impact of a 5/8 inch steel ball dropped from a height of 50 inches.

Innerim	Same as windsor.
Interpupilary Distance	The distance between the centers of the right and left pupil of the person measured.
Iridodiagnosis	Diagnosis of systematic disease by the appearance of the iris; determination of personality traits by examining the iris structure; includes iridology or the study of the structural markings and color of the iris for the purpose of iridodiagnosis. Many claim this to be a pseudoscience.
Karat	A measure of pure gold content in a gold alloy. Example: 24K - 100%. It is unalloyed fine gold. 12K is 50%, 10K is 41.6%. The alloys usually added to reduce the karat are copper, silver, zinc and nickel. The most common material content for spectacle frames was 1/10 12K gold filled, which means 10% of the total weight is 12K exclusive of screw and solder.
Kirstein & Sons, E.	Started in 1864 in wholesale optical business later. Secured many patents in particular the ''Shur-On'' Finger piece mounting which led directly to their leadership in the manufacturing of finger-piece eyeglass frames and mountings; was purchased and name changed to Standard Optical which merged with Shur-On in 1925 to be known as Shur-On/Standard. In 1958 the Textron Corporation brought Shur/On/Standard followed by the 1963 the Continental Optical. The corporation is since called Shur-On/Continental, whose principal product at present is the Corning Photogray lens which at this writing is in short supply. Shur-On/Continental is considered one of the three largest optical manufacturers in America. The others being American Optical and Bausch & Lomb.
Lens	We know very little of the origin of lenses. History indicates that ancient lenses were made of rock crystal (beryl from whence the German word ''brille'' meaning eyeglasses was derived.) Optical glass was not developed until the middle of the 17th century. Rock crystal seems to have been the material of choice for the first 300 years. Rock crystal lenses were available up to and including, the early part of this century.
Leonardo da Vinci	In 1508 he tried to prove a theory. He set up a simple experiment which in basic concept is precisely the basis of how we see through contact lenses and how we apply them. He placed his face in a bowl of water in an effort to neutralize the front window of his eyes, the cornea. The front surface of the glass bowl in effect became the front refracting surface or first transparent surface to focus the entering light as is accomplished by the front surface of a present day contact lens. The water in the bowl served in a similar capacity as the tear interphase in the eye which neutralizes the window of the cornea. This experiment to a man of scientific calling is analagous to the basic principles of contact lenses. Other early investigators as previously mentioned were Rene Descartes, a Frenchman, and John F. Herschel, an Englishman. The latter was an astronomer and mathematician of the era of 1827.
Marco Polo	The claim that he wrote about having seen eyeglasses at the court of Kubla Khan is fallacious and has been denied by Robert Jordan (see Gutenberg's Development) who states, ''No such passage can be found in the writings of Marco Polo. Eyeglasses may have been known in China prior to the 13th century. However, Marco Polo can not be used as source for this claim.''
Metal Houses as against Shell Houses	Metal frame manufacturers as opposed to synthetic plastic frame manufacturers.
Metal Plastic Combinations	A spectacle where the eyewires are zylonite (plastic). The bridge is metal usually gold filled and the temples metal or zylonite. See O.P.C. adv.

Mires	Mires are illuminated reference characters. In this case they are projected by the instrument onto the anterior shiny surface of the eye (cornea). These reflections are observed by the operator. The amount of astigmatism and other abnormalities can be noted.
M. O.	Modus Operandi, method of operation.
Muscle Imbalance	The muscle attached to the outside of the eyeglobe which serve to rotate the eye are not balanced. One set of muscles may be too strong or too weak causing a disturbing additional pull.
Myopia	Nearsightedness, incident parallel rays entering the eye come to a focus in front of the retina.
Natron	A native sodium carbonate occuring in the desert regions of Egypt: Sodium.
Neurologist	Medical specialist in disorders of the nervous system.
Numbered Spectacles	The numbers usually ranged from about the number eight which referred to the focal distance or the working distance to the subject's eyes, to number forty which is even a further distance than is possible to hand-hold a near object. The most common numbers were twenty-four, twenty, sixteen and twelve. In a few remaining states the "glazed goods" law is not yet in effect. Thus permitting the sale of "reading specs" over the counter usually in the "five and dime" stores. The inch numbering system is still used where "over the counter" readers are available. Penn Optical Company of Pennsylvania were the leading producers of "glazed goods."
Numont	A trade name for a reinforced rimless mounting in the form of a bar across the top of the lens which is attached to the bridge or center of the mounting. This bar has a metal of spring tension which is sufficient to hold the lenses in place. The temple portion is attached to this bar.
Oculist	Original name for ophthalmologist and equal in specialization.
Oculo-Muscle Imbalance	The ocular muscles of the eye are not in the correct balance causing under or over convergence or a vertical imbalance. Hence, a poor relationship between accommodation and convergence.
One piece mounting	Same as finger-piece. However, tension is supplied by a flat spring which sets above the bridge of the nose (see Plate #21).
Ophthalmic	Ophthalmic lenses would refer to lenses for vision usage as against lenses for optical instruments. Use herein related to the eye.
Ophthalmologist	Specialist in disorders of the eye.
Optician	Dispenser of prescriptions for glasses written by either optometrists or ophthalmologists.
Optometrist	Specialist in refractive anomalies of the eye.
Oxford	Is a form of eyelgass where a wide flat spring both joins the two eyerims and its tension exerted on the nose serves to hold the unit in place. See plate #31.
Plastic lenses	The author has played an important role in the development of prescription plastic lenses. Back in 1950 in his regular professional practice he encountered a shocking experience whereby one of his young male patients, son of a dear friend, suffered eye trauma as a result of an automobile collison while he was riding his bicycle. After considerable eye surgery the eye was left with a permanent muscular injury whereby the rotation of the eye was limited only to turning nasally. The external motor-ocular muscles were completely void of

182

action. Obviously, double vision resulted when turning the eye in certain quadrants of the visual horoptor. The author vowed to work towards preventing a repetition of such ugly experiences. What followed terminated in the author's development of a method of a combination of both moulding and surface grinding his final polymerized compound into prescription lenses. He demonstrated his development to Lever Brothers of London, England, optical manufacturers who were quite interested. However, they reneged on their agreement with respect to the financial phase. The author was finally able to consummate an equitable agreement with the late Hudson Titmus, scion and head of Titmus Optical Corp. of Petersburg, Virginia. The lens is being marketed under the name of Crystal. Prior to the introduction of the author's development a lesser efficient soft plastic lens was produced in England from Methyl Methacrylate called Perspex. The advantage of all plastic lenses is 1) Safety factor 2) half weight of glass 3) ultra violet absorptive characteristics incorporated 4) 5% clearer than glass.

At about the same time a similar polyester derivative C. R. 39 lens was developed by an optometrist in Pasadena, California and marketed under the name of Armonlite, American Optical called theirs Aolite, Bausch & Lomb-Ortholite and Univis, Uni-lite.

In 1971 the U.S. Military issued a medical directive requiring that all lenses fitted to members of the Armed Forces be made of plastic. The change-over to be within a period of five years. This was a stimulus for other manufacturers to enter into the production of plastic lenses.

Polymer	The product result of the curing of a monomer initiated by a compartible catalyst.
Presbyopia	Vision of old age. The accommodative faculty of the eye recedes gradually the amount coincident with an age group. Texas Guinan's famous cliche, "My eyes are all right, my hands are not long enough." Vision of the fifth decade of life.
Quizzer	A quizzing glass, a monocle of single lens construction used primarily for magnification.
Refraction	The science of eye examination to determine the visual status of the eye and condition of ocular muscle.
Refractive error	Vision deficiency due to the inability of the eye mechanism to focus the incident ray or the ray entering the eye.
Religious Rock	Members of a hippy or "turned on" group who feel that by proselytizing to Jesus, the world will resolve its "Hang Ups." Broadway operetta "Jesus Christ Superstar" (1971) precipitated a great following of the younger community of the Hip generation.
Rimway	Same as Numont, but with an extra screw positioned to hold the lateral part of the lens. The function of the Numont and the Rimway bar is to minimize breakage of lenses especially prior to the advent of plastic lenses. Plastic lenses have a safety characteristic which makes them ideal for any type of rimless mounting.
"Ring on your Finger"	This refers to a common expression encountered by the doctor when explaining the procedure to be followed by the patient in order to insert the contact lens. The lens is placed on the tip of the finger then inserted, lens first, into the eye. Photographs illustrating this method always show the "lens-ring" on the finger: The doctor has known that many a young and beautiful female has had contact lenses prescribed and fitted mainly for cosmetic reasons - 6 months later a proposal of marriage - "a ring on the finger."
"Ripped off"	A condition where the buyer is being charged an exorbitant price.

Saddle bridge	Centerpiece of spectacle which conforms to contour of nose, the height, inclination and depth are variable. Example of measurement NIELS N=Nelly bridge which refers to width. 1 equals number one or 1 mm height. ELS equals extra long shank, other measurements are M for Mary with 1/2, 1 and 1 1/2 for heights. Shanks are regular, long and extra long. This type of bridge was in use circa 1730 to 1925. Within the last decade we witnessed a rebirth of its usage.
Set and Fit pads	This type of pad can be attached to a frame using acetone and comes in a loose form. It serves a useful purpose whenever the frame sits too close to the face. This situation occurs mainly with the oriental and black individuals where the nose structure presents little elevation at the bridge a flat nose.
Shell eyewire and metal center	.100 stock zylonite eyerims and temples with metal (usually gold filled) bridge or center
Shelltex	Zylonite thin rims with centerpieces and temples of metal, clamped at four points of suspension.
Skioptometer	The Woolf Company also developed and marketed a like Dezeng instrument about 1915. A book was published in this connection and authored by Daniel Woolf, "Refraction and Muscular Imbalance." This served to coordinate the thinking of the professionals at the time and thus advanced the adaptation and inclusion of the treatment and correction of this infirmity as part of routine eye work. The treatment of eye muscle imbalance is called Orthoptics.
Snellen Chart	A chart which shows letters of varying sizes premeasured to indicate the percentage of vision.
Storr, Paul	Famous London silversmith and artist of early nineteenth century. In this era originality was lacking. Artisans did little more than reproduce older styles.
Sunvane (Radiometer)	Photosensitive feather weight blades which spin at speeds relative to the intensity of incident sun rays and free=flowing in a clear glass bulb. A modern version of the sunvane is manufactured by Windsor Electronics, Inc. P.O. Box 662 Wheaton, Illinois 60187. It sells for under $2.00.
Swap Meet	As the name implies, a place where people gather to barter commodities. Some set up stands and sell or exchange goods. This is usually held outdoors. A synonym for Flea Market.
Temples	The arm, bow or side piece attached to the end=piece of the front section of the spectacle frame. It can be skull bow which refers to a solid straight side piece or, with a slight bend about 1 1/2'' from the unattached end. The temple end may be bare or covered with a plastic tip. It can also be a solid portion from the front section for about four inches with the balance a flexible cable. The latter for comfort and security of the wearer. Temples are both plastic or metal.
"these G.I.'s just don't cut it"	Attire of G.I. issue is unsuitable; from a letter received by the author from a former patient of his, then stationed in Vietnam. General issue specs varied from flesh colored plastic to grey smoke of .150 stock during World War II and ever since. Those of the Armed Forces with individualistic inclinations just did not "dig" this form of regimentation.
Third Party payment	Refers to the doctor's fee being paid by others than the patient. Such as a union, medical and/or welfare fund, Medi=cal, Medicare, medical insurance, etc. Statisticians claim that within 10 years, 70% of all fees will be third party payment.
Torture Chamber	The pressure required of the spring type of nose bridges caused a considerable indentation on the nose after wearing the eyeglasses for even a short time - The expression at the time alluded to its similarity to the "torture chamber".

184

Trial Frame	A mechanical spectacle frame fitted in front of the subject's eyes containing a grooved arrangement concentric with the eyerims where as many as four lenses can be interchanged by the operator. This system was used to test vision and antedated the Skioptometer. See also DeZeng.
Varsity	Is the original name given to what we know today to be the Oxford.
Visual Angle	The angle subtended by the extremities of an object at a particular reference point in the eye; the entrance pupil.
Weathermen	A national organization dedicated to revolutionary ideals fostering violence as the means of arriving at their goal.
Wells, Edwin P.	First of a long line of principals in the vast empire of American Optical Co. The last reigned in 1967, later merging with Warner-Lambert Drug Company.
Wils Edge	Same as Numont, however, top edge of lens is grooved. The lens slips into a track provided in the mounting. No screws are needed.
Windsor	Frames with totally metal chassis covered partially with thin zylonite. See plate # 1 4
Wires	Most recent terminology for thin metal rims.
Women's Lib	An offshoot of the new ethnic groups. This is a movement sponsoring equalization for men and women in all phases of society. The great appeal being with respect to the relative earning power, and all pertinent issues; an equalization of blatant sexual discrimination.
Young	Thomas Young (1801) was the first to demonstrate the presence of astigmatism in the human eye.
Zone of Comfort	Refers to lens correction which will be both comfortable and offer the best available vision. This can be determined by the extra ocular muscle balance.
.125 Stock	.125 stock refers sheet stock of .125 inches thick.

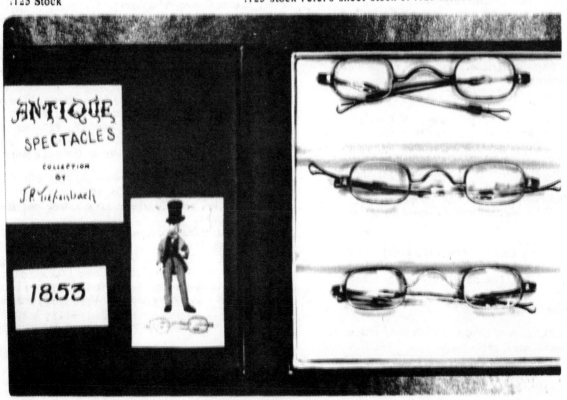

ANTIQUE
SPECTACLES
COLLECTION BY
J.R. Tiefenbach

1853

The bibliography which follows lists a number of recent and some older vintage books on antiques and collectibles both hardcover and paperback. Reference to antique eyeglasses as a collectible is mentioned only in one book. Another, *The Poor Man's Guide to Antique Collecting,* contains a four-page chapter on magnifiers and readers. The author, John Mebane, claims this collectible likely to be "discovered" soon and that the advent of "prescription spectacles" virtually eliminated the need for magnifiers and readers, except for extraordinary magnification, hence their manufacture has been minimized.

The Official Guide to Popular Antiques-Curios by Hal L. Cohen, 1971, page 231, shows an illustration of a "1912 spectacle in iron, brass, silver and gold rims." Retail price range $5.00 to $25.00. *Lock, Stock and Barrel* by Douglas and Elizabeth Rigby, 1944, offers this vignette on page 466 in the chapter on "Some Amenities": A casual reference to old spectacles as one of a number in a valuable specialized collection. This is included with old hats, assorted weapons, wooden legs, Indian arrowheads, and autographed letters." This exceedingly informative book continues and quotes, "It would do little good to offer the collector the moon for any item in his collection."

The author has searched and researched the literature and found an incredible paucity of the written word germaine to the subject. He has deduced from his correspondence and from his scouts that in America alone are to be found a great multitude of collectors of antique spectacles. One day he came across a beautiful lorgnette exhibited in a local antique shop. He inquired as to the selling price. The dealer said it was not for sale. "Why?" he was asked. "I am saving this for Janis Paige, the actress. She is an ardent collector of lorgnettes. I know she will not question my price."

The author hopes this book may serve as a stimulus to those already collecting "specs" and others who may be inspired to start a collection. They will undoubtedly become aware of the great sociological impact "specs" have made upon Early American History and maybe collectors will organize and correspond and learn from each other. Perhaps Nathan Hale's "specs" will be unearthed.

American Encyclopedia of Ophthalmology, Volume VII, Chicago-Cleveland Press, 1915, pages 4894-4949.

American Optical Corporation, *The Story of the American Optical Corporation* (pamphlet #8013) 12/1968.

Barck, Carl, A.M., M.D. *History of Spectacles,* reprinted from the Open Court for April, 1907.

Bausch J.J. *The Story of My Life* (pamphlet) 1911.

Bausch & Lomb *Milestones in Optical History* (pamphlet) undated.

Stamping (pamphlet) 8/1/39.

Bedford, John *Still Looking for Junk,* David McKay Co., Inc., 1970.

Borisch, Irving M., O.D. *Clinical Refraction,* 3rd edition, Professional Press, 1970.

Bradley, Van Allen *Gold in Your Attic,* Fleet Press Corp., 1968

Bronson, Dr. L.D. *Era of Groovy Eyeglasses,* article, Optometric World, April 1971
Plastic Lenses, Modern Plastics, article 1956
Ophthalmic Lenses from Thermosetting Plastic, article Optometric Weekly, 1956; article Optical Journal, 1956.

A Simplified Method of Antiquing Spectacle Frames, Optometric World, December 1971.

Bull, Edward C., O.D. *A Voyage into the History of Spectacles,* American Optometric Association Pamphlet, 1925

Burgess, Fred W. *Silver, Pewter Sheffield Plate,* Tudor Publishing 1947

Carter, John H. O.D. Ph. D. *Phototropic Ophthalmic Lenses,* page 411-412: Journal of American Optometric Association, May 1964.

Cohen, Hal L. *Official Guide to Popular Antiques,* H.C. Publishers, 1971

Cox, Warren E. *The Book of Pottery and Porcelain,* 2 Volumes, Crown Publishers, 1944.

Dover Edition *Steiger Glass,* 1914

Drepperd Carl W. *A Dictionary of American Antiques,* Universal Publishing, 1970
ABC's of Old Glass, Award Books, 1970
Victorian Antiques, Award Books, 1970

Earle, Alice Morre *Customs and Fashion in Old New England,* The Charles & Tuttle Company

Earrick, Alice Van Lear *A Collectors Guide 1790-1840,* The Charles & Tuttle Co.

Eberllin & Ramsdell *The Practical Book of Chinaware,* J.B. Lippincot, 1947

Forster, Dr. Frank *A Doctor's Guide to the Draft,* Lancer Books, Inc, 1970 Section VIII also pages 170-172.

Gardner, John *Antiques and Art Buying in New York City,* The Bobbs Merrill Co. Inc., 1969

Gould, Mary Earle *Household Life in America,* The Charles & Tuttle Company.

Gregg, James R. O.D. *The Story of Optometry,* The Ronald Press, 1965.

Kauffman, Henry J. *Early American Ironware,* The Charles & Tuttle Company

Kovel, Ralph and Terry *The Complete Antique Price List,* 3rd edition Crown Publishers

Lewis, J. Sydney *Old Glass and How to Collect It,* London, undated

Mebane, John *The Poor Man's Guide to Antique Collecting,* Bantam edition, 1971

Orgele, David *Silversmith,* Beverly Hills, California, Catalogue, 1971

National Clearinghouse for Drug Abuse *General Questions about Drug* Abuse, 1970 information pamphlet

Optican - Jeweler, The Volume IV, #34 Oct. 1893.

Optical Manufacturers Association *Standards and Specifications for Marking and Stamping Optical* Frames and Mountings, April, 1971.

Raycroft, Donald R. *Early American Folk and Country Antiques,* Charles E. Tuttle Co. 1971

Rigby, Douglas and Elizabeth *Lock, Stock and Barrel,* J.B. Lippincott 1944

Smith, Marilyn Estes *Collect-Ability,* article in Valley-Wide Press, 11/1971

Thompson, C. J.S. *The Origin and Development of Spectacles,* (Royal Academy of Medicine (Turini) pamphlet Oct. 1934 Connoisseur, 94 pp. 231-239

Twyman, F.R.R.S. *Prism and Lens Making,* Hilgar & Watts, London, 1952

Winchester, Alice *How to Know American Antiques,* Signet Books, 1951

World Book Encyclopedia, The Volume VII *The Magic of Glass,* pp 195-209, Field Enterprises

Univis Coporation *A View from the Bridge,* pamphlet #L458, undated

The News photo

RECONNECTING ornate handle to frame of antique lorgnette is Dr. Louis Bronson of Sherman Oaks. Valued at $300, 1898 item is example of first form of decorative eyewear and part of optometrist's large collection of antique glasses. He wears pince nez style favored by Teddy Roosevelt.

'TREATS' WAX FIGURES

Avid Valley Optometrist Collects Antique Glasses

By ADAM NIEDERHAUS

Patients of optometrist Louis D. Bronson of Sherman Oaks range from actors Ben Murphy ("Alias Smith and Jones") and Peter Lawford to Presidents Washington, Jefferson, John Quincy Adams, Polk, Theodore Roosevelt, Franklin D. Roosevelt and Truman.

While the actors are very much alive and come to him because he specilizes in "mod" frames and lenses, the others are customers in the form of lifesize wax figures residing at Walt Disney World in Florida.

Dr. Bronson's interest in eyeglasses spills over into his personal life through a collection of antique glasses exceeding 500 items, with pieces dating back to wooden Chinese frames of 600 A.D.

It was his reputation as a collector and authority that led to a contract to provide authentic glasses for the bespectacled members of Disney World's Hall of Presidents.

Having begun his collection and study of antique spectacles some 30 years ago, the 55-year-old doctor has encountered an extreme lack of reference material on the subject.

This will be partially remedied in the fall of 1973 when his own book, "Early American Specs," is published.

Results of his research on early eyeglasses and current optometric tech-

niques are made public by his articles in magazines and professional journals. In addition, he serves as associate editor of "Optometric World."

Historic First

Defining an antique as anything made prior to 1830, he admitted that his "hobby" has taken him back considerably farther than that. even beyond the year 1620 in this country.

"That was when a Pilgrim by the name of Peter Brown made a splash by becoming the first colonist known to have worn eyeglasses."

According to Bronson the American optical manufacturing industry didn't get its start until 1826 in the small town of Southbridge, Mass.

"Prior to that everything was imported from Europe. mainly France, Germany and England.

"However, the first pair of bifocal glasses was made for Benjamin Franklin in 1760 from his own plans," said the doctor, who owns a pair identical to the original now in a Philadelphia museum.

While foreign antiques are generally classified by the name of the reigning monarch, such as with Louis XIV furniture and Tudor architecture, he didn't find such convenient tags in writing his book on early American spectacles.

Develops System

Instead he developed his own classification system on the basis of U.S. wars from the Revolution (1775-'83) through the Vietnamese Conflict (1962-present).

"Wars bring about significant changes which some may call progress," he said, "and have had a tremendous impact on spectacle production.

"A very current example is the "aviator" style so popular as sunglasses, which came out of World War II issue to the Air Corps."

Bronson hesitates to place a dollar value on his

Article appearing in

VALLEY GREEN SHEET

San Fernando Valley, California.

collection or individual pieces — particularly in light of the recent upsurge in antique collecting.

"I have a pair of glasses that are advertised in the 1898 Sears-Roebuck catalogue for $2.50. They were recently appraised at $50 and I paid only $10 for them five years ago."

One of his favorite pieces is a hand enlarger made in 1915, molded from solid platinum and now valued at over $1000.

Literacy Factor

While the magnifying properties of a simple lens were discovered centuries earlier, it was not until the middle of the 14th Century that crude eyeglasses began to appear in significant numbers.

In the beginning they were in little demand since they were of little use except for reading — and the majority of men were then illiterate.

The skill of reading spread steadily after the invention of the printing press and by 1629 the demand for eyeglasses was large enough for England to grant a charter to a guild of spectacle makers.

Designed "Status"

Since initially glasses were only used by the literate, it was natural that they would become status symbols worn by people who didn't need them and sometimes couldn't read anyway.

"They were considered a badge of superior social status and learning among the Chinese and an inferior had to remove his glasses in the presence of his superior," said Bronson. "This interesting custom survived in Germany as late as 1915."

They became such status symbols that glasses were "added" in paintings of famous men quite irrespective of the calendar.

A German artist in 1452 showed Moses wearing spectacles and many others thought nothing of including them in scenes of the Garden of Eden. "A painting of the infant Jesus in his mother's arms has the baby holding a pair of glasses supposedly belonging to his father Joseph," said Dr. Bronson.

Aid to Technology

His research reveals an interesting example of how modern technology can explain past events. "Vincent Van Gogh, the famous artist, must have suffered an eye condition called glaucoma, which is quite painful."

While history notes that Van Gogh suffered from pain in his eyes, it remained for his paintings to clinch the diagnosis as glaucoma.

"In all of his canvases the sun and lights are portrayed as having halos, and one of the principal symptoms of glaucoma is a 'halo effect' seen around lights by those afflicted," he said.

5 minute sketch presented to the author

and his son by grateful cartoonist who

created "Goofy" for Disney Productions.

"UH, DR. BRONSON AND SON..."

"THANK YOU FOR THE GLASS TREATMENT!"

7/8/72 Dru Bron......